# Conversations with Raika

First Published in 2020 by:

Fenzi Dog Sports Publishing

© 2020 Denise Fenzi

Cover & Content Designed by: Rebeccah Aube
www.powerupk9.com

Cover Photography by: Nancy Tucker
www.nancytucker.com

Illustrations by: Nienke de Haan
www.pencilandpaw.com

ISBN NUMBER: 978-0-9984066-1-9

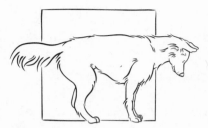

# Table of Contents

Introduction ...................................................................................... 11

## Part One

## Fall 2017

### Chapter 1:

The Lean, Mean, Dog-Show-Winning Machine is Obese! .............. 15

### Chapter 2:

A Highly Trainable Human Who Works Too Much ........................ 21

### Chapter 3:

Have You Noticed How Good My Butt is Looking? ....................... 27

### Chapter 4:

Mom's in the Ditch .......................................................................... 33

### Chapter 5:

Thanksgiving Turkeys and Forced Marches .................................. 37

### Chapter 6:

Walking in the Rain .......................................................................... 43

## Winter 2017/2018

### Chapter 7:

Pinched Nerves, Stolen Toys, and Reminiscing ............................. 47

### Chapter 8:

Raika's First Chrismukkah ............................................................... 51

**Chapter 9:**

Relationship Walks and Hurt Feelings ............................................57

Spring 2018 🌼

**Chapter 10:**

Lucky Finds and Irritable Humans ..................................................61

**Chapter 11:**

The Nighttime Problem...................................................................67

**Chapter 12:**

The Diet is Over..............................................................................69

Part Two

Summer 2018 ☀️

**Chapter 13:**

Get While the Gettin's Good............................................................77

**Chapter 14:**

In Which Mom is in a Coma, or a Plane Crash, or is Kidnapped, or... 81

**Chapter 15:**

Happy Birthday, Raika! .................................................................91

**Chapter 16:**

Ice Cream Cures Toe Cancer ..........................................................95

**Chapter 17:**

Much Ado About Nothing............................................................. 105

**Chapter 18:**

Abandoned after a Life of Selfless Service.....................................111

**Chapter 19:**

Humans Must Not Eat the Dog Treats ........................................... 117

**Chapter 20:**

The Complicated World of Human Behavior ................................. 121

# Fall 2018

**Chapter 21:**

The Great Bedtime Debacle .......................................................... 127

**Chapter 22:**

The Raika-Mobile ........................................................................ 137

**Chapter 23:**

Raika Refuses to Eat .................................................................... 141

**Chapter 24:**

Brito the Sheep ............................................................................ 145

**Chapter 25:**

Snowbirds .................................................................................... 151

**Chapter 26:**

Leashes Should be Illegal ............................................................ 153

**Chapter 27:**

Kidnapped! .................................................................................. 155

**Chapter 28:**

The Walking List .......................................................................... 163

**Chapter 29:**

The Best Gift of All ...................................................................... 165

# Winter 2018/2019

**Chapter 30:**

Raika's Ninja Moves .................................................................... 173

**Chapter 31:**

Pancake Sprinkles and the Business of Sneaking up on People .... 179

**Chapter 32:**

The Five Sisters ........................................................................... 183

**Chapter 33:**

Raika Saves Nick's Life ................................................................ 197

**Chapter 34:**

Molecular Redistribution .............................................................. 205

**Chapter 35:**

Getting Old Deserves a Conversation .......................................... 209

## Spring 2019 ❀

**Chapter 36:**

Mrs. Mountain Lion ...................................................................... 215

**Chapter 37:**

Wandering Raika ........................................................................... 221

**Chapter 38:**

Skunks and Early Walks ............................................................... 225

**Chapter 39:**

Sleepless Nights ............................................................................ 231

**Chapter 40:**

Dying is Not a Linear Process ...................................................... 237

**Chapter 41:**

Proactively Addressing Senseless Human Waste .......................... 245

## Summer 2019 ❀

**Chapter 42:**

The Cycle of Life .......................................................................... 251

**Chapter 43:**

150 Pounds of Expensive Meat ..................................................... 255

**Chapter 44:**

The Substitute Vet ........................................................................ 265

**Chapter 45:**

Raika's Book ............................................................269

## Part Three

## Fall 2019

**Chapter 46:**

Raika's Condition! ........................................................277

**Chapter 47:**

Eat the Best Food on the Good Days ...........................................283

**Chapter 48:**

So Many Pills.............................................................289

**Chapter 49:**

Night or Day, It's All the Same ...............................................295

**Chapter 50:**

Optimism or Denial.........................................................299

**Chapter 51:**

New Vet for an Old Dog .............................................................303

**Chapter 52:**

The Bucket List..............................................................305

**Chapter 53:**

The End of Conversation .............................................................311

**Chapter 54:**

Goodbye, Raika.............................................................315

**Chapter 55:**

And Now We Walk Alone .............................................................317

Epilogue ............................................................323

Author's Note.............................................................325

About the Author.............................................................327

# Introduction

In the summer of 2004, a litter of five puppies was born. One of these puppies was given a red collar, and eventually she was named Raika in honor of her father, Reko.

Raika's destiny was largely bred into her genes. Her mother was a famous competition dog. Her father was a famous competition dog. Her grandparents were specially bred, and so on down the line. As a result, Raika and her littermates held a good deal of promise to become famous - and they did exactly that!

For most of her life, Raika did everything she was asked to do. She jumped when asked to jump, heeled with style, traveled quietly and without complaint, and in short, did all she could to keep her mom happy. She appeared content to follow where life - and her mom - chose to take her. Eventually, she attained the coveted status of Obedience Champion, at which point retirement came. While far from neglected, the dramatic change in her life was undeniable.

And then Raika found her voice, and she had a few things she wanted to get off her chest. Quite a lot, actually.

For a long while, Raika talked but no one heard. She was not discouraged; her many years as a competition dog had taught her to persist in the face of challenge, so she just kept right on talking. And when that voice emerged, it was not nearly as agreeable nor lacking in opinions as one might have thought. Indeed, once she got started, Raika had opinions on everything from what time she went for her walk to what showed up in her food bowl to how she wanted to leave this earth, with plenty of additional commentary in between.

This is the story of Raika's final years; the time when she and her beloved mom found their ultimate relationship to be one of shared companionship rather than about winning competitions. This is a story of life; finding the simple pleasures and appreciating each one of them. This is a story of grace; finding gratitude and meaning in every last day, hour, and minute that you are privileged to share with one another. This is a story of aging; turning back the hands of time until the end looks much like the beginning. And ultimately, this is a story of love; love for a dog that began on the day of her birth and grew ever stronger until the inevitable end, leaving each to walk on alone. And because life without a healthy dose of humor isn't much of a life at all, this is a story of laughter.

If you can suspend reality for a few hours and listen to some conversations with Raika, you will find a good deal of wisdom as she shares her side of things on all that she knows. And as Raika would say, she really knows quite a lot.

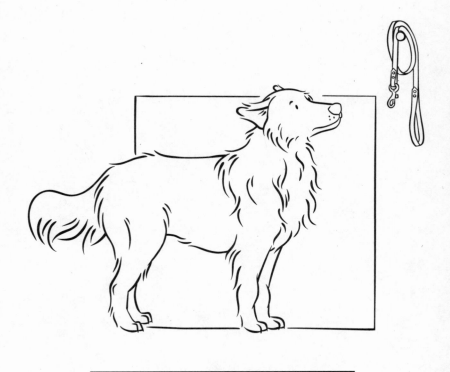

# Part One

# Fall 2017

### Chapter 1:
### The Lean, Mean, Dog-Show-Winning Machine is Obese!

## Mom

59 pounds? Surely that cannot be right. Raika has been in the high 40s her whole life. I figured she'd pick up a few pounds when we stopped training regularly, but there's no way she's worked her way up to 59 pounds. It's not possible.

The vet, oblivious to my distress, has warmed to his topic - care of the aging dog - and moved on to the matter of supplements for joint health, and new and improved medications for arthritis. I've been involved in the world of dogs for thirty years and I already know these things. I'm a dog trainer, for Christ's sake.

Back to the topic at hand. My dog is fat. The irony is impossible to escape; dog trainers are notorious for rolling their eyes at dogs who waddle along looking like seals in desperate need of an ice floe. I know better than to let my dog get fat. How many times have I gently suggested to a client that they keep an eye on their dog's weight? That it's not healthy to be carrying around those extra pounds? Too many to count.

The vet has moved on to the importance of twice-yearly check-ups; catch any pesky issues early! Oh, and her incontinence medication. If she starts leaking, which would be likely at the age of thirteen, we may need to switch to something stronger now that we're approaching the maximum dose.

The elephant in the living room is bellowing, and still the vet has not uttered a word about the matter of weight.

After Lyra and Brito have their checkups, I'll stop by the pet store and check Raika's weight there. This scale must be wrong. There is no way my lean, mean, dog-show-winning machine is cruising at just under 60 pounds.

An hour later, the pet store scale has confirmed that Raika is roughly ten pounds overweight, which is about 20% above her correct weight. My lean, mean, dog-show-winning machine is not just fat, she is obese.

## Raika

**We need to begin with a basic understanding: it's your fault I got fat. Of course I ask for tasty snacks – I'm a dog. You're the human, you're supposed to be the responsible one! You've dug yourself quite a hole where my weight is concerned. Ten pounds. Wow. You must feel terrible about this, which is fine. You should.**

**However, I'm a little concerned about what you plan to do. You're thinking those additional ten pounds need to come off? If I dig deep down inside my rational self, I can see your point of view. I mean, I get it, but we cannot be hasty at a time like this, lest we put my body into starvation mode.**

**If I have to go from 59 pounds to 49 pounds, it's time we get out and about. Since exercise is the obvious route to developing fitness, I am proposing exercise as opposed to food reduction as the primary solution here. Just you and me working out together - how fun! It reminds me of the old days when we were always on adventures together, back before you were running that online dog training school of yours. Oh, and let's leave the little white one and the wannabe Golden Retriever at home to entertain each other. If three is a crowd, I can only imagine what that little saying might suggest about four. Let's make it two. You and me.**

Unfortunately, it's not clear when we can start since I see you've got your suitcases in the hallway. I guess that means you're traveling this weekend?

It's okay, Mom. I understand that you need to do that, but I want you to know that I really miss you when you're gone. I worry that you might not come back. I can't help it. The family is good to me when you're gone, but it's not the same. I sit by the door and think about how much we did together, all the places we went and all the things we learned! We sure covered a lot of territory, didn't we, Mom? Teaching and traveling all over the world! Back then, we always went together, and now you go alone.

Anyway, have a great weekend. I hope you can help those trainers learn to work with their dogs the way you worked with me. A dog can't ask for much more than that.

But I'm still going to watch for you by the front door, just in case you change your mind and come right back or decide to take me with you.

## Mom

Okay... eight meals, carefully weighed out and labeled so there's no possibility of confusion, and what the heck, I'll throw in one more meal just in case there's a travel delay. I will put Raika's food over here on the left-hand side of the freezer so he won't give Lyra's portion to Raika by accident. That would not serve anyone well, in particular my pudgy-wudgy.

Hmm. I'll put her pill organizer by the coffee maker so he won't miss it. Oh! I need to remember to tell him that we're trying a new medication, just in case he notices she has a couple of extras in there.

Perfect.

The goal, of course, is to make it as easy as possible when I'm not around.

"Your wacko dog," my husband says.

It's affectionate - I hear it. But... it's real, too. The truth is, I don't select dogs because they're easy to live with. I select dogs because they are excellent dog sports prospects: high energy, intelligent, and willing. Which certainly describes Raika to a T. But then there's that pesky matter of persistence; I select for that, too, and some days, that persistence makes Raika look suspiciously like an overtired, cranky toddler who isn't getting her way.

Plus, there's no denying that she's my dog. Who wants to take care of a dog who doesn't even like you very much? And with this diet, she's hungry on top of demanding, which doesn't bring out her best self. I know he loves her, but some days she's kind of hard to love.

It's too bad there's no real possibility of bringing her with me. Too much arthritis to stay in a crate for a long period of time, and too grumpy to put up with being left alone anyway.

And then there's that nighttime thing. If she did that when I was traveling, I'd have a heck of a time being even a little bit intelligent the next day. What's that about anyway?! What gets her so upset? And it's so unpredictable! She used to be such a stable dog, a solid working partner, and now...

I hope the vet is wrong about the possibility of dementia. That just seems incredibly unlikely; she seems so normal and engaged most of the time. Just that weird panicky thing on occasion.

"Wacko," he says. Well, the fact is I owe that "wacko" a lot, even if she is a bit troublesome to take care of these days. Heck of a nickname for a dog who was a significant part of my career success.

God, how did I let her gain so much weight? How did I not see that coming? Ten pounds! I still can't believe I let that happen. Amazing how easily I let food substitute for attention. Not that she was complaining.

"Hon? No snacks for Raika. And since it wouldn't be nice to give Brito and Lyra snacks without including her, none for them either."

I feel like Scrooge, especially with the Holiday season coming up fast. At least I'll be home for the Holidays.

"Sure. Run off and leave me with your starving dog. And no, I won't sabotage her diet while you're gone."

He'll try. We'll start there and see what there is to see.

## Raika

You came home! I'm so relieved. Did you have a nice time? Did your students learn a lot? I took care of things around here for you so you didn't have to worry too much. I simply don't know how Dad would manage without me.

Boy, I'm so glad you're back, Mom! I'm feeling fresh and ready to go! Are you happy to be home, too? I hope we'll be heading out for some exercise tomorrow. I'm so excited to have you home that I'm going to sleep extra close to you tonight and check on you frequently. I know you're tired, so I'll let you get some sleep now. Welcome home!

Oh! And if you're wondering about my diet, let me tell you, it was like military school around here. I tried all the tricks - begging, sighing, staring at the stove where the extras were - and nothing worked! The family was a veritable wall of resistance against one helpless dog! I had to go to bed hungry every night, just like a homeless dog, except I was in the house, of course.

Anyway, now that you're back, we will be starting our new fitness routine, right? I'm ready! I'll stay nearby so you won't have to look for me when the time comes.

# Part One

## Chapter 2:
## A Highly Trainable Human Who Works Too Much

### Raika

I'd like to thank you for the newly implemented exercise walks. It's been about a month now, and I wanted you to know that I enjoy them! See how I understand positive reinforcement for humans? I'm starting out with what you're doing well! I do, however, have a few random concerns that I'd like to bring to your attention.

One issue is a matter of quantity. We've had a solid handful of walks so far. That's a good start! However, on the day it rained, we didn't walk at all. That means we need a make-up policy. You can't just skip them and pretend like it didn't happen. Not that I'm beating a dead horse or anything, but I have ten pounds to lose because of your negligence.

And if one begins to speak of quantity, then we must be ever mindful of the corollary, specifically the matter of quality. In human years, I am about 80 years old. You, also in human years, are only 48. Yet, you're a little bit... well, nothing polite is coming to me, so I'll be blunt: you're slow. I feel stifled. The logical thing is that you need to start running.

Yes, I've heard about your bad knees. But between you and me, that's silly. You are half my age. You can run. It's only half a mile to the start of the trail, and then another half mile on the way back. Once the leash comes off, you can hobble along like an invalid for all I care, but I really need you to move a bit faster.

And while I'm talking to you, I'd like to bring up an unrelated matter.

I would like you to stop emptying the wastebasket next to your desk, the one where you put pieces of paper. I enjoy shredding those random bits, and it's such a small thing for you to clean up at night. I was very disappointed today when I went to the trash and could not find even one item to shred. Is it asking too much to let an old dog tear up pieces of paper when you don't have time for me? I know that when the human kids were young, they made much bigger messes than I've ever made with my paper shredding. Considering I spent the vast majority of my life making time for you, I'd imagine you would be eager to either reciprocate or to provide a consolation prize - like a full wastepaper basket.

Anyway, I hope you will go ahead and make these small changes now so that I can be mentally engaged and healthy for as long as possible.

*Mom*

I love my dog, I love my dog, I love my dog.

It's totally true, and maybe if I say it enough, I won't feel the urge to kill her when she's demanding a walk in the middle of my workday. Her preferred techniques - resting her head on my leg, sighing, tapping her foot - she's making me crazy with all of them!

Of course, it works. Isn't there an expression about the student becoming the teacher? Well, apparently I'm a quick study because eventually I cave, get her leash, and out we go. Her consistency and persistence are things to behold, but it makes it hard to get things done. Plus, she doesn't seem particularly discouraged by much; neither darkness, inclement weather, nor my workload seem to factor in at all. I'm being trained at a record pace, and I know about training - God knows I've been doing it long enough. I wonder if she perceives me as a highly trainable human - qualities to be selected for in an owner?

She looks right at me and practically talks to my brain. "I'm bored! I'm bored and you work too much! I have ten pounds to lose because of your negligence. It's time to go!"

And I listen. How can I not?

The thing is, she's right. I work too much. Everyone says so. I'm either working, thinking about working, or finishing work. And if I'm finishing work, then I'm probably heading to bed, since work is all-consuming and exhausting. From the computer to the phone to the tablet; I'm working all the time, whether at home, at an appointment, on an airplane, or out for a walk. Good thing I love work. Good thing my family loves me.

Of course, an argument could be made that all that work and no play is making Denise a dull girl. Time to get a little shine on my dull exterior and take a true vacation! Except... the thought of not working makes me a bit panicky. I might need to start small in the vacationing department. Speaking of a vacation, how does one even make that happen with an old dog who requires non-stop care and attention?

Walking might be just the ticket - baby steps. Get me up and out of the house. Next step: vacation. Or possibly therapy, whichever is cheaper. And takes less time away from my work. By that argument, Raika is helping me; I bet she'd enjoy that perspective.

Yesterday my husband asked me, "Do you enjoy your Raika walks?"

That kind of depends on how you look at it. For sure, the exercise is benefitting both of us, but I don't much enjoy walking in inclement weather. And while I mostly let her lead the way at her pace, it can be shockingly fast for an old dog.

Until, of course, it's not. Like when she stops dead in her tracks, fascinated by some random rock or patch of grass or God knows what that causes her to refuse to move - sometimes there's not even anything there! But I don't allow a whole lot of that; these are supposed to be exercise walks, after all.

Then again, I have a chance to respond to my texts when she stops, and I do appreciate that. Because if I'm being honest, a whole lot of our walk takes place with me on my phone and it can be hard to get anything done when she's flying along.

So here I am with my thirteen-year-old obedience champion, being trained to provide what she wants when she wants it. Except for food. I'm holding the line there.

It's actually kind of amusing if the dog trainer in me doesn't think about it too much.

## Raika

**I'm really proud of you, Mom. That was quite the effort you put out today. There is room for improvement, but wow! You must have run at least halfway to the starting point of our walking trail, and maybe another little bit after that! Look at you!**

**Now, to clear up a few misunderstandings.**

**I know this was your first run in a long time, but your references to the story of the tortoise and the hare were ridiculous. That business of the slow and steady turtle winning the race against the hare? That never happened. That was make-believe.**

**What really happened is that the hare ran circles around the tortoise, leaping back and forth over him until the poor thing had a heart attack. I'd hate to see that happen to you, so I thought that if I put a little tension on the leash, then it would help your feet move faster. Which, I might add, they did! And for all of your complaining, I'd like to point out that you did not fall over, have a heart attack, or "croak" on the trail, as you suggested might be your fate if we continued at our briskly refreshing pace.**

**In spite of this miscommunication, I'd say that on balance**

it was a good day - a solid B+. Thanks for stepping up the pace. Have you thought about taking me for a weigh-in? I feel like I'm doing pretty well.

Part One

# Chapter 3:
## Have You Noticed How Good My Butt is Looking?

### Raika

Since I know you're a fan of speaking openly, I think we need to get right to the topic of numbers. I forgot to pee and poop before I got on the scale today. That right there could account for a solid pound of misunderstanding. And everyone knows that if you lose weight too quickly, it's not healthy! Since it took me over a year to gain this weight, I think it's reasonable to assume that it will come off over about the same period of time. Too much too soon might shock my system, don't you agree?

And no doubt you have considered the matter of relative weight; specifically, muscle weighs more than fat! Surely my exercise walks have increased my muscle? Speaking of muscle, have you noticed how good my butt is looking?

Finally, the pet store scale could easily be off by at least a pound, so let's avoid making decisions based on potentially unreliable data. I recommend we maintain the status quo, and take another look after my next weigh-in. No more eyeing my breakfast bowl with a frowny face!

By the way, since we can both see that I'm getting more fit, if not more thin, we should discuss the questionable snacks you've been doling out - specifically, the vegetables - and the potential ramifications to you. As a result of your stingy choices, you should probably know that if you leave a bowl of food unattended somewhere, I will almost certainly feel inclined to help myself. I won't feel bad about it either, even if such behavior would never have crossed my mind in my more youthful years. So if the question, "Wait, did I just see Raika take that?" should happen to cross your mind, I want you to remember the vegetables.

## Mom

I saw the whole thing.

Chris put his backpack on the chair and then set about making his after-school snack. He cut a few pieces of cheese, placed them on a slice of bread, added a few more leftovers from the fridge, topped it with the second piece of bread, and put the whole thing into the panini sandwich maker.

Raika sat near his feet, watching intently.

He then filled a glass with milk, grabbed his sandwich, and headed for his room, Raika following closely on his heels.

Next, Chris placed the sandwich on his desk out of reach - he's showing awareness! Of course, this is a new habit for everyone; Raika used to be so good, but these last couple of months, she's become a thief.

Keeping one eye on his screen and the other on his sandwich, Chris started working his way through his Instagram account.

Raika gently tapped her foot on his ankle to remind him of her presence. Her hungry presence. He continued to ignore her. Excellent! He's learning! It reminded me of how she behaves with me when she wants to go for a walk, except that I cave. Look at my son holding strong; he'd make a good dog trainer.

Halfway through his sandwich, he stole a quick glance in her direction only to see a thin string of saliva dangling out one side of her mouth reaching halfway to the floor. His expression suggested that he thought it was pretty disgusting.

I wondered if he could sense that she was following the movements of the sandwich, from his mouth to the plate and back again, becoming progressively more concerned with each bite.

Raika shifted with impatience. I saw him look at her, pause, and then resume eating the last quarter of his sandwich. We're almost there. Hang tight, son!

Two bites left. The thin string of drool made it to the floor, forming a small puddle on the side of his shoe.

He looked around his room, carefully avoiding Raika's pleading gaze.

And then it happened. Just as I was about to congratulate him on his excellent execution, he placed the plate on his desk and reached behind the computer to plug in his phone.

It's over. Raika snagged the last bite and was gone before he even looked up.

At least I have an excuse; I'm going to blame the kids if anyone looks twice at Raika's rounded appearance. Maybe that's not 100% fair, but who said life is fair?

## Raika

**Two pounds! Now we're talking! That's some real weight loss right there; I feel so fit and free! And that's in spite of the fact that I stole a chicken nugget! Well, maybe it was a few nuggets, or maybe even a full tray. For the record, no one seemed to be eating them.**

**Lest you judge, I'd like to point out that I haven't always seen your willpower shining brightly either. Just because you were born with the thumbs and I'm the dependent doesn't mean the issues aren't the same. I've seen you eat an extra bowl of ice cream for dessert or start out with just one nugget - or cookie - and then finish off the entire plate. A little sympathy goes a long way in a situation like this, you know.**

**Thanks for not yelling at me over the nuggets when you discovered your loss, even though I could see you were frustrated with yourself for letting that happen. I**

**understand, Mom. When I make mistakes, sometimes I spend too much time thinking about them too. We should learn to just let stuff like that go. Something for you to work on, even after I'm gone - letting go.**

## Mom

Whatever happened to the old-age progression that the vet warned me about? Where is my slow and arthritic dog, dragging along behind me, refusing to eat even the most tempting foods? This thirteen-year-old dog can outwalk - no, outrun - me! For four miles?! And how the heck did she get those chicken nuggets off the stove anyway?

Maybe other dogs get old in some kind of predictable fashion, but not this one. If I didn't know better, I'd say she's just coming to life.

I see a silver lining for sure. My own health and fitness has certainly taken a backseat seat to almost everything these past few years: family, dog shows, training, and of course, work. However, I was expecting the occasional day of rest to allow my muscles to recover and I've yet to see my furry taskmaster get behind that idea. She appears to have her own plan that leaves little to no room for things like my opinion, and when push comes to shove, Raika has a way of winning these failures of consensus. Who wants to go out in the rain anyway? Raika, of course, that's who.

On the other hand, when we're out walking, she can't roam the house getting into trouble. For a dog who's never gotten into the trash or taken a thing off the counter, she's certainly taken a "hold no prisoners" approach at this point in her life. I've never been one for superstition, but maybe the number thirteen gained its unsavory reputation via an incorrigible elderly dog, because that is pretty much the exact age that Raika became a demonic, paper-shredding, counter-surfing, attention-seeking tyrant requiring non-stop supervision.

Well. Maybe not demonic. Actually, she's awfully cute with those bits of white scattered throughout her muzzle, and the light, milky blue tint to her eyes - a few reminders that she's not a troublesome toddler as much as an old dog.

# Part One

# Chapter 4:
## Mom's in the Ditch

## Mom

What could possibly have possessed her to get into a dogfight? Honest to God. She's an old dog! I'm still trying to wrap my head around this whole thing; she's never done such a thing in her entire life!

Maybe the other dog bumped her or something? Caused her some pain? Honestly, it all happened so fast that I don't know what to think. I was standing there, chatting with the other owner and smiling benevolently at my old dog meeting her friend, and then wham! Next thing I know, everything is happening a mile a minute - fur flying, dogs snarling, and I'm in the ditch. I'm seriously mortified about the whole thing. For a dog who never even looked at other random dogs to end up in a dog fight while being walked by her dog trainer owner... I'm trying to hold on to the humor of the situation, but I landed in the ditch!

She's fine. I'm not. I'm a little sore, but mostly I'm mad! What was she thinking! I know she's old, and I know that sometimes old dogs do weird things but a dog fight?!

I'm going to soak in the hot tub. Might help me from getting stiff. Help me to forget. But that might take a while.

## Raika

**You seem to be feeling better this morning. Maybe just a touch grumpy? Is it your body that hurts or your ego? I think you should take some Tylenol to help with that. Well, the body part anyway.**

**So. About my indiscretion yesterday. I'm not trying to make excuses, and I take total responsibility for my**

behavior, but I want to give my side of the story.

For starters, I have always liked that dog! Every time we've met, she's been just fine; we greet, have a little play, and move on. No worries.

So why did she do that stupid jumpy thing right in front of me? She startled me! I thought she was going to land on me or get aggressive or something.

It was supposed to be one quick warning snap and lunge so she'd know that wasn't okay. I had no idea that she'd take me seriously! And then what was I supposed to do? I mean, at that point, it's not like I could just walk away.

On the plus side, our walks have increased my fitness enough that I could respond - good thing she didn't trample me! That is a good thing, right?

Admittedly, the rest is a bit fuzzy, but I do want to apologize that you ended up in the ditch. That must've been a little uncomfortable for you, especially when the guy fell over on top of you. At the least, that must have been awkward? But you weren't really hurt, were you?

Maybe we should consider the bright side for a moment. Tally up all of the positives!

For example, it's a darned good thing the little white dog wasn't with us. That would've been a disaster! He's crazy. I'm not sure what he would have done, but for sure I don't know how you would have managed all of that.

And no one had to go to the vet or the human doctor! Just a few scratches here and there, nothing that can't heal up lickety-split. See, we're all okay! That's what matters, right? That everyone is pretty much okay? Just like you tell the kids, "It's a good thing no one got hurt." Well, no one got hurt a lot. Just little hurts. The kind that will make us all a bit wiser in the future.

In hindsight, I can see that I probably overreacted a little, and I'd like to apologize for that. I could have backed off instead of snapping. But once we got started, I sort of forgot everything I was doing. I wasn't making very good choices anymore. In fact, I can barely even remember what happened; it's all a blur.

I say we can chalk this whole thing up as a learning experience. And learning is always a good thing, don't you agree?

Wow. I'm almost thinking it's a good thing this happened!

You don't think so?

Wait. I have an idea. Why don't we talk about something else? Like, for example, how terrible the ticks are this year. Have you noticed it, too? I think we should probably do something about that. Put all of our thoughts and energy into solving the tick problem.

Okay. You're not ready to talk about something else.

Maybe this is one of those things that we should sleep on. Sometimes the mad doesn't go 100% away with one good night's sleep. But if everyone gets another good night's sleep, I bet we'll all feel better in the morning.

And while I wait for you to get sleepy, I'll just lie here quietly at your feet, keeping an eye on you. You do know that I love you very much, right Mom?

So when you're not mad anymore, maybe you could give me a sign. You know, when you're ready to talk.

You're smiling again. That gives me hope.

I'm still a good dog, Mom. I just made a mistake. It won't happen again.

# Chapter 5:
## Thanksgiving Turkeys and Forced Marches

## Mom

I really do love a good deal, and wow - today was all about the good deal! Just look at the price per pound on this turkey! Well, turkeys, since I actually bought three of them. Holidays are amazing for a great deal; I couldn't walk away. Lyra and Brito can eat turkey for the next few weeks. Or maybe months. Years? They're not on a diet, very fit and trim, the both of them.

Though thinking more, Raika may complain if she sees the others eating turkey and she doesn't have a serving for herself as well. I wonder what I could give her? Maybe some of the other things from a traditional Thanksgiving dinner since I did buy all the side dish options as well. Possibly a bit of stuffing, a drizzle of gravy, and some green beans to fill up the rest of her bowl. If I mix it up so the flavors blend, maybe it will fool her into thinking she got some turkey. Oh, and I need to remind the kids not to give her food from the table.

I wonder if Raika will even notice she's not eating turkey? On second thought, no... only a delusional person would think Raika wouldn't notice. She's not a fool. "Pain in the ass, demanding, wacko dog," as the husband would say - yes. But a fool? Not so much. This is Raika we're talking about.

I need to think through this a bit more.

## Raika

**I couldn't help but notice that you purchased quite a lot of food yesterday, including several turkeys that are much too large for you to eat with the family, even if you decided to invite the entire neighborhood. I take this to mean that the holidays are now upon us? Now, without being overly**

dramatic, I'm a little concerned that I might get left out of the bounty, being as I'm on a diet and all. So to be clear, because sometimes I've noticed that subtle references don't always get through to you, what you need to know is that if you try to dump green beans and a touch of gravy in my bowl and call it good, there will be hell to pay.

We need to remember the importance of tradition in relation to holidays! Specifically, the traditions concerning the canine members of this family. Even more specifically, the tradition of sharing food as a sign of love and caring! Conversely, we know that withholding food is punishing. No one wants to punish the ones we love, so let's be thoughtful about how we proceed in the coming days and weeks.

Another universal holiday tradition is that everyone puts their diets on hold. Since I am a longtime faithful member of this family, I assume that I will be included... right?

One other thing. As long as you're maybe listening, I'd like to remind you of some of my personal favorite edibles from the holiday eating season. Cooked turkey? Tasty! A bit of gravy on top? Delicious! Go ahead and give Lyra the turkey neck, and the little white dog can have the leftover green beans since I certainly don't want them. Lord knows you've given me enough vegetable filler foods recently. Yes, green beans are good enough for Brito.

Now, let's talk about holiday exercise. In the past, there was often a family walk while the turkey cooked. But now I go for a walk every day, so out of respect for the holiday, we need to do something special in addition. My suggestion would be a family walk in the afternoon, which has nothing to do with our morning walk with just you and me. That's our bonding time, remember?

I'll be waiting patiently at the door tomorrow morning, and again in the afternoon. Looking forward to a wonderful day!

## Mom

My husband says we need to get the family up and moving, and he's right, lest the kids spend their entire holiday vacation staring at their screens. They need to get out. Well, at least Nick does, and Chris needs more family time. We either make it happen or watch as they grow roots into their chairs.

Time to step up my parenting game and be a role model! Leave my phone behind, stand up, and go! Well, I might hang on to my phone for emergencies and decisions that need to be made sooner rather than later. But the youngsters can manage for a couple of hours without their phones.

Of course, they'll refuse. They say no to pretty much everything. No wonder people walk their dogs - dogs want to go! So much excitement at the thought of spending time with you! Teenagers? Not so much. So we can't suggest; we have to inform. Make it a familial obligation. We'll tell them straight up that we're going for a walk - and no phones. We're taking the dogs! Everyone is coming! A family adventure!

Man, I do love dogs. Grateful for every morsel of attention they receive. Well, most dogs anyway. Raika's kind of unique in her demanding and self-centered way. Which is okay; she's old. I do love my cute-old dog.

Then again, the kids are usually fine once we get them out the door. Maybe they're even begging for the attention and structure that only a parent can provide - deep, deep down inside.

We could try that walking trail behind the retirement home. It might be a little busy during the holidays, but it's not too long, and it's relatively flat. That will give them less to complain about while they find their appreciation for nature. Or come to grips with the inevitability of family bonding.

Our next dilemma is who to bring. Three dogs and four people is a little overwhelming. On the other hand, walking out the door without the dogs seems kind of mean-spirited, and Raika needs all the exercise she can get, so we can't leave her behind. We can give each kid a leash and I can keep Raika. See how that goes and adjust as we gain experience.

We'll give it a shot. Get everyone out and away from the house a little more this holiday season. It'll be good.

## Raika

I have mixed feelings about these holiday walks - or "forced marches," as the younger members of the family refer to them.

On the one hand, it's pretty exciting to be part of the group, and it certainly pushed up the excitement level by a factor of ten or so. Leashes tangled, kids arguing, observers scattering at our approach. I think my favorite part was probably when Brito stepped on that patch of wet grass. You should have called him "Marshmallow" to account for his reaction to getting his feet wet, like he was melting from the bottom up! Get it? Little white dog? Marshmallow, because he melts in the rain? I really do have an amazing sense of humor. Look at me go, just full of puns and witty little bits - I really do crack myself up. Too bad you're not listening; surely you'd enjoy my sense of humor?

Oh! Or maybe the best part was when I acted on my overwhelming urge to leap up at your face as an expression of my enthusiasm for being out and about. That was kind of fun, too. Speaking of leaping, I should probably apologize for that even though I'm not actually sorry. I was simply overcome with joy and felt a need to express it; repression leads to nothing but anxiety. Maybe it will help you to see it as a cathartic event as opposed to a training failure?

On the other hand, there's nothing relaxing about being clotheslined by the leashes of overly zealous family members who can't manage to walk a dog in a straight line. By all appearances, an observer might think you needed to hire a good dog trainer. Have you considered instructing the rest of the family on how to work with a dog? I don't think I've heard our names said quite that much in the entire previous month.

"Lyra, no! Lyra, come! Cooome! Come here!"

"Brito, stop. Brito! BRITO!"

Not once did I hear a recognizable command that we could actually follow - just "No!" this and "No!" that.

Let me just say this: I'm glad you had my leash.

Anyway, I sort of missed the quiet rhythm you and I have, moving steadily along without much fanfare.

As I add up the pluses and minuses, I'm going to suggest that we do the occasional forced march to get the youngsters out and about, but when we hit the end of the holidays, let's keep it just you and me, okay?

# Chapter 6:
## Walking in the Rain

## Raika

Four days and no exercise walks.

Ostensibly, this is because of the rain. The little drops of water that fall from the sky. The little drops of water that have been falling from the sky since time began.

In case you're being dense, my point is that a little rain is no reason to skip our walks.

In the not so distant past, we had a routine. It didn't matter if it was blazing hot or freezing cold or raining buckets. We trained regardless, because that was what we needed to do in order to succeed. Do you think I enjoyed heeling with my face turned up to watch you while the rain splashed into my eyes and water ran into my nose? No, I did not. I did it for you because I'm a good dog. I was cooperating.

Then pray tell, Mom, why is it that when it's my personal exercise walks on the line, the ones that I love, you're suddenly unable to go out in the rain? Is this newfound tendency to melt in water in any way related to the time you've been spending with Brito the Marshmallow?

I have only one word: raincoat.

It worked fine before, and it will work fine now.

Remember, it's your fault I picked up these unhealthy extra pounds. Now we need to pursue my exercise needs with the same single-minded determination you applied to preparing for competitions.

If you're not sure where your raincoat is, I can almost

certainly help you find it. My guess is that it has petrified dog treats in the pockets, which are almost certainly several years old by now. I imagine I could find it by smell alone. Heck - even you could probably find it by smell alone, and I've never been all that impressed by your sense of smell. I say we start looking this very afternoon.

## Four hours later...

Mom, I'm almost speechless with pride! I mean, this is solid A+ territory!

I totally see how you got fooled - I didn't expect rain when we started, either. There would have been no reason for you to bring a raincoat. So when it started to pour, I was prepared to cut the walk short, to turn around and go back. And despite what others might say, I'm not heartless. I understand that sometimes plans don't quite work out, and I can appreciate that we tried.

But you didn't go back! You kept going! You didn't reach for your phone and call for help. What courage in the face of adversity! I honestly didn't think you had it in you. You walked in the pouring rain with no raincoat or even a proper jacket to protect you. Amazing!

Indeed, it seemed as though once you had adapted to the fact that you were going to be completely soaked, you relaxed and really had fun. I thought you looked kind of proud of yourself, splashing through puddles like a ten-year-old. Well done, Mom!

For myself, I was practically giddy with excitement when I saw that our walk would continue. Then I remembered that I'm too old to be quite that enthusiastic. But then I remembered that I'm not like other old dogs! It occurred to me that maybe I should jump up and bounce off you a few times to express my enthusiasm for your excellent

**choice.  Then I remembered that you don't always appreciate that, and it was pretty muddy out there after the deluge.  But I couldn't let this go without letting you know how much it meant to me.  Methinks you're warming up to our exercise walks, which is truly excellent.**

Mom

So much for a "slightly cloudy fall day with cool breezes and a chance of showers in the afternoon." More like the monsoon season in the tropics.

Though in hindsight, it was actually pretty fun. Out on the trail with not a soul in sight - what difference does it make if I walk in the puddles or even splash through them a bit? And anyway, I couldn't have ended up any wetter than I was after the rain started to come down by the gallon. And Raika? Raika was beside herself, leaping and running and playing like a puppy. Her enthusiasm is infectious when she gets like that. Some days I watch her when she's happy and silly, and I think I could not love her any more than I do. But then the next day comes and indeed, I love her just a little bit more.

I'm warming up to these exercise walks. Can't say I'm glad I let her get chubby, but I am enjoying our time together.

# Winter 2017/2018

## Chapter 7:
### Pinched Nerves, Stolen Toys, and Reminiscing

## Mom

Poor Raika. Hopefully that prescription will help her with the pain, but the part about keeping her home and quiet? No walks for a few weeks? Man. That is going to be hard. For both of us.

And of course I wasn't here. Why do bad things always happen when I'm not around to help out? Murphy's law strikes again; head out to travel for work and the old dog gets hurt - the one who can least afford it. The vet said it's probably a pinched nerve and will resolve on its own with time and rest, but still, I wasn't here.

Anyway, I'm home now and not planning any travel for the next few weeks. I'll be here to get us through this.

Oh well, at least I can work nonstop while keeping an eye on her. As long as she keeps hanging out under my desk, the supervision part will be easy - but I'll miss our walks. And of course I'm worried about her.

## Raika

**I wanted so much to go for a walk with Dad while you were away, but we stayed home after he took me to the vet. I know it was the right thing to do, but I'm still disappointed. It was bad enough that you weren't here when it all happened - not that I even know what happened. I woke up just like normal and the next thing I know, I had this terrible pain that I couldn't ignore, so I**

went to Dad's side of the bed and woke him up to get some help. He tried to make me feel better until he could call the vet and get me an appointment, but Dad isn't you.

Just so you know, this stupid neck problem has been there forever, but this was much worse than it's ever been. Dogs are pretty good at hiding pain, especially when there is something we want to do. Heck, I've seen you work right through a bad headache and no one but me even knew about it. I do the same thing and don't let you know lest it cut into my fun time.

By the way, I really appreciate how you've been keeping the wastepaper basket full for me. So many things to shred while I recuperate! However, I couldn't help but notice that Brito has some small, soft, stuffed toys. You know - the ones in his pen? They look really nice to hold and chew. I was thinking it might make me feel better to hold one in my mouth while I fall asleep, just like he does. I know that sometimes I forget to treat them right and remove all of the stuffing. But isn't that a small price to pay to keep an old lady dog happy? They don't have to be new or expensive toys. Just soft, stuffed, pet-store-sale-bin toys for me to hold at night when I go to sleep.

Alternatively, since my attempts to communicate with you have been slow to show results, I could just steal those little toys from his pen when you forget to shut the door. Yeah, I think that's what I'll do.

Mom

She's hurting. I hate that. I'm grateful it's nothing more than a pinched nerve, but that doesn't change the fact that she had to go to the vet when I wasn't home. I need to start thinking about lightening up my travel schedule, which isn't going to be easy.

Though look how cute she is, sleeping under my desk holding those little stuffed toys. Speaking of those little stuffed toys, she must be getting those from Dad. I'll have to remind him that those are for Brito.

I admit I had a momentary thought of going for a walk without her, but then I looked at her and... I can't do that. It would be wrong and I bet she'd find out. She seems to know everything.

What I can do is catch up on a whole lot of work. I need to get back to it.

## Raika

I've just about had it with the resting. How much longer do I have to rest? There's nothing to do, and when I'm not doing, I'm thinking. And sometimes thinking turns out badly for everyone. I'm tired of reminiscing about the past. Will I be allowed to go out again soon? Tell the vet that I feel really good and I'm not even lying. It's time to get back to our exercise.

When I was young, I was the most amazing athlete! Remember when I learned how to dive into a swimming pool head first and go all the way to the bottom? I've never seen another dog do that. I do love diving. As soon as summer comes, I'll go back to it. You'll watch, right? I only like to dive when you're there to watch me.

I sure did a lot during my life. How many sports did I compete in, five or six? I think so. I'm not complaining. I've had a pretty full life.

Well, crap. There I go again, wallowing in the past.

Thanks for staying home with me when I didn't feel well, but I'm definitely ready to get back to our exercise routine now. Maybe tomorrow? I'm really much better! No need to check back with the vet. Let's just go.

## Mom

Raika is healthy enough to resume her regular activities! I didn't even have to beg or grovel for permission, though I might have gone that route if the vet had suggested extending her rest. I just couldn't have taken much more of that huffing and puffing from a stir-crazy old dog - it could blow the house down! Okay, maybe that's an exaggeration, but it is not an exaggeration to say that she's challenging to be around when she's not getting her way.

I think she stirs up the other dogs when she's bored, which leaves everyone on edge. When Raika is not happy, the entire household is not happy. Just when I get totally engrossed in my work, the dogs start to make a nuisance of themselves, and when I look to see what's causing it, there she is, watching, like some kind of overlord making it all happen.

What part of my brain thought that this was going to be an opportunity to catch up on my work? There was no catching up. None. I spent most of my catching-up time patting her head and telling her it would be over soon. Back to your bed, Raika! And off she would go, for approximately 30 seconds, only to return with those staring eyes and tapping feet.

The vet did say we have to start out slowly. Frankly, I'm not sure what that means. Start out slowly? Who? The dog or me?!

Here's my prediction: I predict that all of that rest will have given Raika's muscles a chance to heal and grow stronger. She's going to be on fire when we get out there.

And my own muscles? Floppy dead fish.

Man, how does she know? I haven't even picked up the leash yet and I can feel her watching me. She knows I'm thinking about her, and I'm not even looking in her direction! How does she do that?

Anyway, after our walk, I think I'll take Brito over to the pet store and pick up a few things. He'll enjoy the outing and I don't want to overdo it with Raika.

## Chapter 8:
### Raika's First Chrismukkah

Raika

Having given Brito a thorough sniff, can you explain why
you took the little one to the pet store instead of me? The
vet has cleared me from bed rest, after all, and I am both
willing and available as both your trusty companion and
shopping consultant. I cannot imagine what he brings
to the table. I mean, if you take him, then you might be
focusing on all the wrong things. Besides, who cares what
he thinks?

Eh. Who wants to talk about Brito, anyway?

I want to talk about me. Specifically, I want to talk about
my Hanukkah wish list. Yes, Hanukkah. It appears that
the gifts start earlier and last longer than for Christmas,
so I'm signing up for that program this year. Admittedly,
Hanukkah is almost over, but I'm thinking we could split
the difference and start today - sort of a hybrid holiday
celebration. We can call this "Chrismukkah."

With a good deal of soul-searching, self-sacrifice, and free
time while I rested on my dog bed, I have gotten my gift
list down to only eight items which, coincidentally, is the
number of days of Chrismukkah. I've done my research,
you know.

Mind you, the list started out quite a bit longer. Seeing
as I have already whittled it down to the bare essentials, I
imagine you'll want to get me all of the things listed here.
Yep - every last one.

Here's my list:

A new dog bed, just for me, that you can place under your desk. I'm not sure how you'll keep the other dogs off it, but since you're such a famous dog trainer, you'll figure something out.

A soft, squishy toy with extra removable stuffing. We might want to buy a six-pack so they'll last till the end of the holidays.

A rubber dog toy. You know, the indestructible ones that make you say bad words at night when you step on them? In spite of your gloom and doom predictions, you still haven't killed yourself stepping on one, so let's bring them back.

Knucklebones for chewing. They make my teeth shiny and keep me occupied for hours. Throw one in for Lyra for good measure. See how giving I am?

A big bag of meat dog treats, the soft ones. I'd like either pork or bison, please. No fish.

A calendar for the new year and a red pen. With a calendar on prominent display in the kitchen, when we miss a walk due to bad weather or some other excuse, you can circle the day in red so that we don't forget to make it up later on.

A bark collar for the little white one. Or, if you find that unpalatable, train him to shut up. Consider training Brito to be quiet as one of the greatest gifts you could give to me.

This last present is very easy! I want ALL of the wrapping paper for the holidays placed in the wastepaper basket. It makes the most amazing sound when I shred it! That could keep me occupied for long stretches of time while you do your work.

In case you run out of money and need to buy food for the human family, you can leave off Lyra's bone.

I'm excited for the holidays to arrive! And don't forget that the food rules are relaxed for family members on holidays... EIGHT DAYS worth of holidays, to be exact! I should have converted years ago!

Oh, and Mom? I did think up one more thing; one more Christmakkah present that I would like to have, but this one does not come from the store. It simply takes a bit of extra time. It would be wonderful if we could go on the occasional "sniffing walk" instead of our usual "exercise walk." On a sniffing walk, I can go as fast or slow as I want. Don't worry. I don't mean that we'll be running the whole time. But it would be fun to occasionally sprint to a bush that smells especially intriguing. Some of our sniff walking might actually be pretty darned slow, because it would be my chance to get to know my neighborhood better.

On the best sniffing walks, we might not go in just one direction. For example, let's say I stop to sniff at the eucalyptus tree, and then we move on. But then I remember something I forgot to check. On a first-class sniffing walk, I could go back to that tree and take another quick sniff. Instead of walking with a purpose in only one direction, there might be a bit of backtracking here and there. You could think of it as a zen exercise for yourself: you have to give up going forward in order to go forward.

Raika the philosopher; I like it!

I realize we couldn't do this all the time - you do have to work to pay for my dinner. But sometimes, when work is a little slower, or when it's a special day, could we give it a try? And since the vet has cleared me to resume my regular activities with a slow and steady start, this would appear to be the perfect time to begin.

**Speaking of resuming regular activities, I hope you noticed that I didn't go screaming through the house with sheer joy when I heard the news that my bed rest was over. Remarkable restraint if you want my opinion. Anyway, it's time to get back out there no matter how we do it. My number one holiday wish has been granted!**

## Mom

My husband thinks Raika should get the holiday off from her diet. I, however, have concerns.

You know that expression if you give an inch, they'll take a yard? That one has Raika written all over it. And while a professional dog trainer probably shouldn't admit that the old dog gets what the old dog wants, there is some truth to that.

I mean, what happens if we open the door to a non-dieting day? Today, it's a few extra morsels in her bowl, and tomorrow it's a personal Uber to the grocery store. So, to suspend the diet or not to suspend the diet? That is the question.

Look at her there, eyeing her food bowl and tapping her foot to make sure I'm aware of its obvious emptiness. Or maybe to add emphasis to her starving plight? I'm not sure.

On the one hand, I can only imagine how hard it is for her to smell those delicious cooking foods and get so little for herself. And all I have to do is go along with my husband's Raika-friendly proposal; I don't even have to participate! Softie that he is, he wants to take over feeding her. Just for right now.

On the other hand, we're doing so well with her diet! At this pace, we'll wrap it up in just a few more months. If we start adding holiday food to her bowl, how is she going to understand when the holidays are over?

Of course, the rest of the family will go back to eating regular food and she will go back to eating regular food as well, so that's a pretty clear sign that the days of feasting are over. Not that her regular food is terrible since I prepare her meals at home and she's never eaten a kibble in her life, but still, home-prepared lean chicken is not turkey with gravy.

## Raika

What a holiday!

A full breakfast - very normal and perfectly tasty. Then a walk with the little white one in tow. In and of itself, that was unfortunate. But then I learned that you bring delicious food when The Brito comes along! And that food was even tastier than my breakfast! Next up? Lunch! What a fabulous treat! I never get lunch! Ham and turkey fat and some other very tasty bits!

Last but not least, the pièce de résistance, dinner! On top of all that breakfast and lunch, I got turkey and stuffing, gravy, biscuits and butter, cranberry sauce, bacon crumbs, more ham - you can never have too much of that - and all the things mashed up together!

I'll admit that when I saw that turkey come home a few weeks ago and saw you chatting with Dad while looking at me, I was afraid for my well-being! However, it appears you either thought things through, or the family bludgeoned some sense into you. Either way, I had absolutely no complaints about my holiday culinary options, regardless of who actually put the food in my bowl.

Oh! And that doesn't even include the presents that you brought home from the pet store. I'm going to start breaking in my new dog bed right now while I work on digesting my dinner. Wow, Mom. I never really expected that you would get almost everything I asked for. Thank you so much!

I see you got a new holiday toy, too! I am hoping against hope that this thing is going to serve me better than the birthday gift you received earlier this year. Remember those shiny running clothes? I thought you looked great, and I had high hopes. Sadly, they didn't make you run any faster. I don't know if you were disappointed, but I sure was.

Now, this new thing tells you how far we are traveling, right? For the record, I did not laugh when you discovered that your walking speed was within inches of your running speed. Honestly, I can't grasp how this could have surprised you. But I have faith that this new toy will allow us to take longer walks and see more places. The important thing is that you're trying. Look, if you want to put a positive spin on it, why don't we just agree that you walk really fast instead of saying that you run really slow?

Just in case I haven't told you lately, I want to thank you again for our special walking time together - just you and me. I can't quite bring myself to thank you for my diet, however - even in this season of thanks. Maybe someday I'll look back on this time with a different perspective. Or maybe it will remain seared into my memory as The Time of Famine.

Oh, and out of curiosity, is Brito's bark collar on backorder?

# Chapter 9:
## Relationship Walks and Hurt Feelings

## Raika

I'm down six pounds since the start of The Hunger Games (or, as you call it, my diet)! Wow! I knew it was time for a weigh-in!

The Hunger Games, along with walks, have been going on long enough that I think we can agree that something is working. I am losing weight. Not only that, but look at how fit and strong I'm becoming! Isn't it amazing how a few months of walks can make such a difference?

Since exercise is now just part of the daily routine, what would you think if we stopped calling our time together "exercise walks," and started calling them "relationship walks" instead? It seems to me that the nature of our walks has changed. Do you feel it too? I think we've had a chance to get to know each other even better during these past few months. It's so much more than just losing weight, especially when you put your phone down and pay attention to me. Anyway, think about it. And while I know we haven't started the sniffing walks yet, I have hope that you might come around on those, too - when you're listening a bit more carefully.

When is our next walk anyway? Maybe... now?

## Mom

I knew that losing weight would make Raika even faster and put a greater spring in her step than before, but what I did not know is that I wasn't going to reap the same benefits at the same rate. She's getting younger - and me? I am not.

How can my running speed have devolved so much? I have always run a ten-minute mile. I know it's not a blistering pace, but I was consistent. How is it that Raika is getting faster while I'm getting slower?

In fairness, I'm definitely getting more fit, but I had expected more carryover from my younger days. I mean, look at Raika! For every pound she loses, she seems to drop another year of age as well.

Clearly, if we keep up these regular walks, she'll be around for a good long time, and we haven't even entered the swim season yet! I've always been amazed at what swimming can do for a dog's weight and fitness. This might be the year to beat all years for her overall conditioning, which is saying a lot.

If I'm honest with myself, I'm really quite proud of that dog. So what if I'm not keeping pace; she's amazing and watching her is worth a lot, even if I can't hold a candle to her abilities. We just need to keep up her fitness plan and keep her healthy and young!

## Raika

**That feeling you're having now, Mom? That feeling of remorse when you know that you have done wrong? I hope you're suffering.**

**You got my hopes up! You took out a leash and put on your jacket! And then, instead of inviting me out the door, you took the stupid little white one.**

**Were you thinking about me and my unhappy face, watching at the window for you to return, as you went off without me?**

**Shame on you.**

**What, exactly, has The Brito done to deserve the privilege of going out first? Just in case you've forgotten, let me tell you: he has done exactly NOTHING. Not one ribbon on**

the wall. Not one burglar scared away. Not. One. Thing.

The oldest dog goes out first. That's the rule. I should not have been left home alone feeling like you forgot all about your loyal dog who has devoted her whole life to serving your interests.

I hope you're miserable every moment you're out with him. I hope he screamed and ate garbage and threw his useless body at every dog that passed by, causing you endless embarrassment.

It's fine that you do stuff with him, though if I were you, I'd probably spend more energy teaching him to shut up around the house than worrying about exercise. But that doesn't change the basic rule – old dogs first. Young dogs last.

Then, to add insult to injury, who did you leave me for company? The Golden Retriever stuck in a Belgian body: Lyra. Someone needs to tell her that life is not all rainbows and unicorns.

If you come up with an extra-long walk and a heartfelt apology accompanied by a tasty snack, then I might be able to start the process of mental healing.

## The next day...

It's possible that I overreacted yesterday, Mom. I'd like to apologize for that, and I want to thank you for the nice little bone you brought back from the pet store for me. I like marrow bones, although I noticed that this one was missing most of its stuffing. You should complain to the store when that happens.

I didn't mean all those things I said about the little white one. He's not stupid. And the part about him throwing his small body at the other dogs and embarrassing you? I didn't mean that either. I know you worked hard on that and he's doing fine now.

As far as the Golden Retriever masquerading as a Belgian? Most of the time she's actually pretty good company. It's just that when I'm in a bad mood, I find her endless good cheer a little irritating. It would be helpful if she could learn to read my mood a bit better and adjust accordingly. Though how this family ended up with a dog so lacking in powers of observation is beyond me.

On balance, it ended up being a pretty good day. I still think you might want to work a little harder on Brito's barking, though.

## Mom

I admit, there was a little voice inside my head suggesting that it was probably not such a good idea to walk Brito before Raika. So I guess I wasn't totally surprised when I got back and Dad told me that Raika had spent the whole time staring out the window, looking miserable. It didn't help that he was on her side, pointing out that the old dog should get to go first.

My plan was to take her later in the day when it was a little warmer, but I certainly see where I erred. She barely looked at me all day, and of course I felt terrible about the whole thing; quite the indiscretion on my part. Hopefully the new marrow bone and extra long walk got us back on solid footing again.

# Spring 2018

## Chapter 10:
### Lucky Finds and Irritable Humans

### Raika

I am a well-trained dog, but I am not a guide dog. If you rely on leash tension to allow you to look at your phone rather than paying attention to where you are going, don't be surprised if you wander into things or trip on rocks in your path. It is true that I am always out front, but that is where a dog is supposed to be! So the next time you ask me if I walk six inches in front of your feet to "take you out," I'd like you to consider an apology and come up with a more charitable explanation. And anyway, I assume that one of my jobs is to protect you from whatever might lurk around the next corner, and it's hard to do that if I can't see what's coming up.

If you want my opinion, you shouldn't be looking at your phone anyway. You should be paying attention to me. This is supposed to be our personal time together; our chance to bond and become even better friends than we already are! Don't ruin that. You can look at your phone when you get home. Yes, even when it vibrates, since that seems to be your downfall. Maybe next time you could just leave it home altogether?

My whole life, I've heard you say that if people want their dogs to pay attention to them, then they need to pay attention to their dogs. Admittedly, I'm not training for dog shows anymore, but why should that change?

To give you credit, I've noticed that you're improving in this area, and on some days you have, indeed, left the phone in your pocket the entire time. Was it so bad? You seemed to survive well enough without slavishly jumping to attention at every little buzz. How about we make that a regular thing? There's just no need to pull it out and stare at it every time I stop to sniff a new spot. These walks are supposed to be our time together so we can look at stuff and enjoy a little nature.

Now, I know you're not feeling too well today which, presumably, explains why you're wandering around the house looking miserable, dusting things and the like, rather than walking me. And if I'm being charitable, I could imagine that on a day like this, a phone might be handy in case of an emergency. So I'd like to suggest that we go for a walk even though you're not feeling great. I am a pet. I need a walk! And there you are, acting mopey and tired, ignoring my hopeful face.

Think of it like this: if you feel sick while we're walking, you can just stop and let me sniff around until you feel well enough to continue. You can even keep your hand on your phone - while it remains in your pocket - so you can call for help if there really is an emergency. Besides, if you do manage to pass out, it's better if it should happen in public where you can get help, rather than alone at home with only me, beset by my own age and problems.

Wow. If you actually did faint out on the street, boy, would I have a story to tell! And believe me, I would tell it. A lot!

"Remember the time we were out walking and you passed out, and the ambulance came, and...." I almost hope it happens, just for the great story it would make!

So anyway, what do you think? Put away the phone, suck it up, even if you're feeling a little queasy, and let's go for our walk.

## Mom

I don't know why it took me so long to figure out that I could drive Raika to new trails. I love seeing how happy she is; she looks like a puppy. So adorable! Except for the matter of eating horse poop. And rolling on dead things.

There sure is a lot of horse poop on those trails, and my unfavorable opinion certainly carried no weight once she discovered that culinary delight. Presumably, this is because she believes she's starving and must scavenge to survive. How many calories are in an ounce of horse poop anyway? Maybe the internet can tell me... On the other hand, if I run a Google search on the nutritional content of horse poop, my internet advertising profile may never recover. Scratch that idea.

Just a few more pounds until we can focus on maintenance, so that is definitely something to look forward to. Maybe that will take care of her random eating choices when we're out and about. What a nasty habit.

The vet said old dogs often stop eating and start getting sick, yet she's never sick and she'll eat almost anything I hand over - plus, of course, her lucky finds. A freak of nature. How can she be almost fourteen?

If I'm completely honest with myself, it would be more accurate to say she's an example of better living through chemistry. There's quite a collection of drugs keeping her spry and comfortable. Which is fine - that's my plan for my doddering old age, as well - keep the doddering out of the equation for as long as possible and focus on the spry.

Speaking of the vet, I should get her back in to see about those panicking episodes. How she can go from a sound sleep to shaking and clawing her way up my body is beyond me.

As far as the rolling, if there's something dead, she certainly manages to find it. And wow - what a smell. I don't even know how she can live with herself until I get her home and cleaned up.

## Raika

Some days, you're just plain irritable. I used to think it was logical cause and effect, that I did something that was rightfully annoying to you, but now I'm rethinking that idea. The fact is, your moods are not necessarily rational.

Take today, for example. Why do you care if I make a snack of a few road apples? Horses eat grass, so they can't possibly have that many calories, and I find them tasty! Yet you're always trying to make me leave them alone.

You need to learn more about intestinal ecology. Bacteria are important! It's a very normal thing for a dog to want to add bacteria to the gut, and it's not like I'm asking you to eat them with me. I think the expression "live and let live" applies nicely to this situation.

And the rolling business - which is, after all, my business - it's not like I find crippled animals and then smother them to death. They're already dead! Indeed, the more dead, the better! So I'm not seeing the problem there, either. It's just like eating the horse poop. It's part of the natural cycle of life. That's why I roll on the dead things and squeeze some of that delicious smell on my body; then anyone and everyone will know where I've gone and what I've been up to. As an added bonus, the dead thing gets further smushed into the ground, helping with the decomposition process.

Hey, that might be my first five-syllable word. "Decomposition." Good one, no?

Anyway, what is your contribution to the cycle of life? Squeaking, "Eww!" and walking faster? Help me understand how that contributes?

As far as the obligatory after-roll bath, let me just say that I thought I smelled delicious, and so did every other dog who had the privilege of coming within 50 feet of me.

Not only do I smell delicious, but I'm becoming ultra fit as well - I do look amazing for my age, don't you think? Just that bit of distinguished grey on my muzzle and over my eyebrows, but otherwise, I look like a youngster!

Back in the day, I was always the fastest, strongest, and most athletic dog out there. I know I won't ever get back to that kind of condition, but that's okay. We can both pretend that I'm getting younger again.

Today really was a fantastic day. I feel so strong now, and I love our extra-long walks in new locations. This really is the perfect way for us to spend time together, exploring the occasional new trails with that cell phone firmly in your pocket. I didn't know that we could go so many different directions when we left the house - we just need to head for the car! Where else can we go? Do any of the trails have water for swimming? That would be about as good as it could get now that the weather is warming up a bit.

When we ran into that man on the horse, I realized that all of those years of training together did more than make me a famous competition dog; they made me a really great dog all around! I was so proud to hear that guy talk about me. It's true, isn't it? I'm a good dog. By the way, I was listening when you told that guy you weren't the boss, that we're a team. I loved that. I'm glad you see it that way. I've always thought that we were a team, too. I even refrained from eating horse poop while you had your chat, just in case he shares your opinion about that matter.

Now that we're walking regularly, I think one of my primary jobs should be suggesting other ways to look at things. After all, I am an expert on a dog's point of view. I hope you appreciate my efforts. If nothing else, I will give you some ideas that you might be able to use, although I do kind of wonder if you're listening.

Can you hear me at all? The more I talk, the more I find I have to say, so I hope you're paying some kind of attention. Who woulda thought I was so full of ideas and conversation? Well, that's rhetorical - I always knew I was full of ideas and conversation. However, the more I practice trying to get you to hear me, the more I feel my personality coming out. Anyway, give me a sign if you can hear me. Something. Anything!

And since we're chatting, or at least I am anyway, sometimes I think you don't have enough to worry about so you create problems where none exist. If you ever start listening to me, know that we might have found a prime area of improvement for you! Don't make mountains out of molehills. Eating horse poop is a molehill, as is freshly rolled perfume on my fur.

You may want to write those down.

# Chapter 11:
## The Nighttime Problem

## Mom

I wish I had an answer to her nighttime problems. The vet is pretty sure we're looking at old-age dementia causing both the panic and sleeping issues. Or maybe she has pain where we can't find it. I hate it when she's clearly upset and I don't know how to help her, but since it only happens at night and it's quite sporadic... eh, what's a weird night every couple of weeks? I can deal.

Having an old dog is definitely weird. It's like she'll be doing great, and then out of nowhere we have one of these nighttime episodes, or she soaks her dog bed with pee, and then I remember - she's an old dog. A healthy and fit and feisty old dog, but an old dog nevertheless.

We did figure out the link between the smoke detector and panic though, so that's good. We can make sure to keep fresh batteries in it. A very manageable solution for sure.

And look at how the weight is coming off! We're almost back to the status quo, which will be fantastic going into the summer swim season.

The whole family will be happier when she's off her diet. Frankly, I think they've missed slipping her the occasional snack. Who doesn't like to share with an appreciative audience?

## Raika

**Bedtime starts out fine, but then I can't get comfortable. I try getting up, I try lying down, I try different parts of the room, I try everything. I go to bed when you do, the same as I've always done, and then I curl up on my bed at your side. No changes there.**

But I just can't stay asleep. I know that I'm disrupting everyone with all of my comings and goings. I can't even explain it to myself, so I can't explain it to you.

It's not that I have to go to the bathroom. Well, sometimes I think I have to go, but after you let me out, I don't really have to go after all. And sometimes I think I'm thirsty, but as soon as I take a sip of water, I know that's not it. So, of course, I come back to bed... but then I want to go back out again. Maybe it will pass. Sometimes bad things go away on their own.

I am not complaining or asking for help, so this does not warrant another trip to the vet. Frankly, I'm sort of mortified by the whole thing, so this is the one time I'm glad you aren't listening to me. Or at least you don't appear to be.

And about the pee. I barely know where to begin about the peeing matter. I have no idea how it keeps leaking out of me. There I am, lying on my bed all comfy, and when I get up and walk away there is pee all over the place! I know it's mine. I can smell it. But I do not understand how it escapes. This never happened before. I'm peeing on my own dog bed! To make matters worse, the stupid little white one doesn't even understand that it's an accident. He thinks it's an invitation, and now he's peeing on my dog bed, too!

These things didn't happen when I was younger. Getting old isn't easy, is it?

Chapter 12:
The Diet is Over

## Raika

Eight whole pounds!  Incredible!

You know, Mom, we could stop this diet right now.  We
both know that two pounds isn't going to matter in the
greater scheme of things.  If it's important to you, I can
stay on the diet; I'm used to it.  But those two pounds?
Aren't that big of a deal.  I'd love to have a little more to
eat each day.  What do you think?

This past year of my life has been pretty darned good!
I've always loved the things we did together, but now
it's like we're real partners.  Team Raika!  As a matter
of fact, there are times when I almost think that you can
actually hear me talking to you.  You look at me as if you
understand.  But then something else happens, and I'm
pretty sure you're not listening at all.  I'll keep trying
though - it's become a habit to talk to you.

Our relationship has changed, and it's not the weight loss
that caused that.  It's the time we're spending together.
Surely that doesn't have to stop?  Indeed, it's more
important than ever!  I'm getting older no matter when we
end this diet.

I wonder if you understand that.  Sometimes I think you
confuse how I look on the outside with the aging process
on the inside.  Looking younger doesn't mean I've become
immortal.

Hey, I have an idea!  How about little snacks throughout
the day to keep my blood sugar on an even keel?  For
example, when you see me staring at the kitchen counter,
that will be my way of telling you that my blood sugar is

falling under the optimal level. That would be your cue to hand over a snack. It can be small, not too many calories. You know, just a little something to help tide me over until my next regular meal?

And don't worry! I won't take advantage of you. Mostly. But it wouldn't be a terrible idea if you moved a dog bed to the kitchen so that I could be more comfortable when I do my counter-staring. Just in case it takes you a while to notice me sitting there. Staring. Being hungry. I'm practicing now. Are you watching? Listening to me?

## Mom

Raika looks amazing. I think she might be one of those dogs who sticks around to a record old age. I hope so. I'll just keep right on walking her - she's still walking four miles every day! Tough girl for sure.

And hey, look at me! Walking four miles every day right along with her, even in bad weather, leaving my cell phone in my pocket. Mostly.

At this rate, maybe I'll stop working long enough to consider a true vacation. No cell phone, no computer, no nothing; just let that online school run itself! Take the family to Australia and explore the Great Barrier Reef, far from the internet and civilization!

And watch my carefully developed business run itself into the ground? Hmm... might need to think this through a little more before making concrete plans.

## Raika

Seriously?! The diet is over? Mom, that is the most amazing news ever! What's for dinner? What about breakfast? Will there be snacks, too? Will I be allowed to lick the frying pan like I used to? Wow! What a first-rate day!  More food for me!

What about the walks, Mom?  Will we keep going on our walks?  Of course, with summer coming, we'll add in swimming, but I don't want to let go of our walks.  I hope they mean enough to you that we can keep doing them even now that I've regained my athletic figure.  There's so much to explore in nature!  Every day is truly a new adventure, don't you think?

I'll admit I'm a little nervous right now.  I know I look good; I've watched your expression these last several months, and I can see the relief on your face as I've lost weight.  But I'm a little disappointed, too.  I'm trying not to be discouraged, but I do wonder.  I have been trying so hard to talk to you about some very important things.  We need to talk about the future.  Mom, looking good doesn't mean I'm getting younger, and walking every day will not create immortality.  I'm getting old now, and someday I am going to need you more than ever.  Are you getting ready for that time?

Sometimes you look at me, sort of tilt your head, and then you look a little harder at what I'm looking at.  That's when I have hope!  I think to myself, she's listening!  She's really listening!

So I haven't given up yet.  I'll just keep right on talking, and hopefully, someday, you'll talk back.

## Mom

Raika?  Can you hear me?

Raika, last night I had a dream.  In my dream, you were talking to me.  But I wouldn't listen to you even though I knew that you wanted to tell me something important.  I woke up with tears streaming down my face because it was so clear what you were trying to say.

In my dream, you were tired. You tried to stand up but it took too much effort, so you lay back down.

I sat next to you, but I couldn't look at your face because I didn't want to see what I would find there. My beautiful girl was tired of living; tired of life. No amount of walking or changing of diets could make you young again. Still, you persisted. You wanted me to see that you weren't happy to be here anymore. That you were too scared and confused to stay with me any longer. You wanted me to let you go - to let you walk on alone.

I sat by your bed, and every few minutes I touched your head gently. I could tell that you appreciated that, but it wasn't enough.

And then I woke up. I patted your head as you lay on the floor next to my bed. You looked up at me and I looked at you - really looked at you - to see what I would find in your graying face. I was so relieved to see you confirm that it was a dream, that it wasn't your time yet.

Life demands effort from you now, whereas in the past it was simply life, effortless, not anything you had to think about. Knowing that your life has become harder fills me with fear.

It is a consolation to me to know that your medications are working. You're comfortable most days.

That dream, though... It makes me wonder if I will be strong enough to hear what you are telling me when your time comes. Will I be strong enough to let you go, or will I prolong the inevitable? You will die someday, and that day will be too soon regardless of how many more years we spend together. The best I can do is to make your remaining life as much about you as possible.

Raika, humans do not hear well when they are talking. We need space and silence to open our senses to details that we normally miss. During this last year of our walks, I found the silence that I needed.

I've thought about all your requests, some of them easy, some a little inconvenient, others... well, just plain Raika.

Yes, Raika, I'll keep the wastepaper basket full for you. We'll take lots of walks, explore new trails, and I will keep fresh batteries in the smoke detector so that the beeping noises won't scare you. I will hold you close when you start to panic, even if it's only in your mind - because it's real to you. I will only take you to the vet when it's absolutely necessary, and I will never leave you there alone. As for rainy days? Now that I've found my raincoat, we need never miss another walk just because of a little rain.

And when the time comes that you will be ready to leave this earth, I will try very, very hard to listen so that I can hear you when you tell me that you've had enough of this life. I'll hold you then, too. And I will miss you forever.

In the meantime, we will walk together every day, and I will work to be open to the lessons that you may still want to share with me.

Now I am listening, Raika. Now I can hear you.

# Part Two

Part Two

# Summer 2018

## Chapter 13:
### Get While the Gettin's Good

### Raika & Mom

**Good walk today!**

Glad to hear that, Raika. What did you like best?

**The half-eaten glazed donut stands out for me. Sorry I didn't share.**

I didn't want any part of that donut. You found it in the dirt. Plus, I was a little annoyed that you ate it even after I called you away from it.

**I came when you called. I took the treat you gave me and everything.**

Yes, I know. And then you went back and ate the donut anyway.

**I thought you were offering a particularly good deal. First, I get a cookie for recalling past the donut, and then I get the donut - a cleverly designed training setup - all so that you can prove to me that coming when called can result in fabulous and unexpected rewards!**

I called you again when you returned to the donut after taking the treat from my hand; did you hear me?

**I find that the presence of donuts makes my hearing a little weak, in particular when I notice you glance down at your phone rather than supervising me.**

Weak, my ass. You snagged that donut and swallowed it in two seconds. That looked more like "get while the gettin's good" than a hearing problem.

**For sure another possible interpretation. No matter, though. With my new, svelte waistline, the occasional donut isn't going to matter. I simply had dessert before dinner on this very fine summer day!**

I'm more concerned about your general disregard for following rules than the actual donut-eating.

**That's very controlling of you.**

Rules exist for a reason.

**Mom, everyone knows that the socially acceptable thing to do with the aged is to give them free rein over their ever-shrinking destinies, and encourage them to kick up their heels a little. What difference does it make if a doddering old lady requests a candy bar for dinner? I presume you would hand it over with a smile, grateful to see her enjoying herself. And since it's faster for me to help myself than to ask, I would hope that you would simply smile with benevolence as I went scavenging for tasty morsels at my advanced age. Frankly, I think you're more annoyed about not getting your way.**

**On another note, we're having a barbecue today? Does that mean burgers for dinner? I like burgers. And a swim? It's a warm day. A swim would be just the thing to keep me comfy. Plus, it's good for my figure. Got to keep my butt in shape, you know - especially after eating that donut!**

Raika, I'm not okay with the scavenging because you could end up sick. At your age, a run-in with the wrong bacteria would be bad news. Or maybe we're not visiting the vet frequently enough for your tastes?

I see we're bringing out the big guns in this discussion. Resorting to threats!  No need to bring up the vet.  I'm doing great - you keep saying so!  Plus, just a minute ago you said the problem wasn't so much the donut as the not listening.  You should work to keep your stories straight.

# Part Two

# Chapter 14:

## In Which Mom is in a Coma, or a Plane Crash, or is Kidnapped, or...

### Raika & Mom

**So you're leaving me?**

I'm not leaving you.

**I see suitcases packed and standing in the hall. You're leaving me.**

Raika, I'm not leaving you. I'm traveling.

**So I'm coming with you?**

No, I have to work, so I'm going and you're staying here.

**I'm pretty sure that "going" and "leaving" are synonyms.**

The way you say it makes it sound like I'm abandoning you forever or something.

**Abandoning me?! Wow. Talk about inflammatory word choice. If I had said something like that, then there would be room to quibble. When are you coming back?**

Well, I'll be back on Sunday night, but then I leave again on Monday morning, so you'll barely see me.

**I'll see you. I'll be waiting by the side of your bed for you to return. As I always do when you're gone. Where are you going?**

For the weekend I'll be in Canada, and then next week I'm going to Japan.

**Japan is a long way away. Are you sure you're going to come back?**

Raika. For the almost fourteen years you've been alive, have I ever not come back?

**Well no, but by definition, if you hadn't come back you couldn't be leaving now, so that proves nothing.**

All right. I'm coming back. Okay?

**Maybe. We don't know that yet.**

Would you like to wish me a good trip?

**Have a good trip. Without me.**

Close enough. Be good to Lyra and Brito, okay?

**Both of them?**

Yes, both of them.

**I'll think about it.**

Raika, it's going to be okay! You have the dogs for company and Dad is here to take you out for walks and swims.

**It's not the same! Sometimes he goes the wrong way and he doesn't know the people we're supposed to stop and talk to.**

You and Dad can create your own walks and activities when I'm not here. I'll be home in about two weeks.

## Lyra & Raika

Hi, Raika.

**Hello.**

Where's Mom?

**She left.**

Do you know where she went?

> **Far away. She might not come back. For sure it's possible. Planes fall out of the sky, humans get hit by cars, kidnappings happen - there's a lot of ways to die when you're traveling and you don't have your dog to look after you.**

She'll come back, she always does. Are you going to sit here by the door the whole time she's gone?

> **Maybe.**

There's nothing you'd rather do?

> **This is not about me; it's about Mom and her absence, and who knows what might happen next?!**

She just left this morning.

> **Do you think kidnappings only happen after days or weeks go by? I can't believe you're going to be in charge of Mom's welfare after I'm gone. She won't make it two weeks. I bet your optimistic spirit gets everyone killed before my body's even cremated.**

Well. Good luck with your vigil.

> **A vigil?! It appears that even you recognize the seriousness of the situation. Small comfort that will be when we hear the news.**

## Lyra & Raika

Good morning, Raika. I see Mom is still gone.

> **Yes.**

Why does she go away for so long?

> **She says she has to work. By now, I would imagine they**

**may never recover her body, especially if she died in a plane over the ocean. Or maybe she's in a hospital in some godforsaken place. Or a prisoner. Forever.**

Raika, she's not dying in a hospital. You can see Dad reading her posts on Facebook, and if she were dying in a hospital, he would be there with her. But she's not here, that's for sure.

**I want Mom to come home. I miss our walks. I miss our swims. I miss our routine. I miss the random trash that I usually manage to scavenge when we're out and about.**

It'll be fine, Raika. She'll come back. She always does. And anyway, Dad's been taking you out pretty regularly; you're not suffering nearly as much as you're letting on.

**What do you know about suffering, anyway! You and Brito - you don't know about suffering the way I do. Let me tell you about suffering! When I was a pup -**

Raika?

**- we had to train every day. Sometimes, we even -**

Raika! I know the story; I've heard it hundreds of times.

**Even the part with the rain? And the snow and ice?**

I know all about the rain and the ice, and it doesn't snow here.

**Ah, well. Old age embellishments.**

Go find Brito and tell him the story. I'm going to look for Dad and see if he'll take me out for a swim.

## Raika & Lyra

**She's dead.**

Raika, she is not dead. Mom just isn't home yet.

**Or maybe lying in a hospital bed somewhere, comatose.**

Mom is not in a coma.  She'll be home soon.  I know it.

**Possibly, or maybe she's already dead and buried.  Some irony if she dies before me, considering I'm the old one that everyone worries about.**

Raika!  She is not in a coma, not dead, and not buried!  Where is your optimistic spirit?

**Comatose.**

Just look at the humans.  Everyone is happy.  The kids went to school, Dad went on a bike ride, and we're all doing normal things.  That would not be happening if something terrible had happened to Mom.

**Maybe they're trying to hide it from us so that we don't panic.  Then one day, they'll just spring it on us out of nowhere.**

Wow.  You really are a pessimist.  I am not a pessimist.  I prefer to look for the good in every situation.

**Yes, Lyra, I've noticed that about you.  I think you're lucky to be alive, the way you see good lurking in every dark alley.  You need to know the world is a dangerous place!  You can't be too careful!  That's my motto, anyway.  And look at me being alive after almost fourteen years - clearly I'm on to something.  I wonder if Mom let her guard down and someone killed her while she was busy being optimistic?**

Raika, listen to me!  Mom is fine.  You'll see.  She'll be home very soon now.

**I think I will resume my vigil by the front door.**

Your new dog bed would be more comfortable.

**How could I possibly think about my comfort at a time like this? Do you think Mom is comfortable in the cold, hard ground?**

If you're not using your dog bed, I think I will.

**Get that idea out of your head lickety-split.**

Raika & Mom

2 p.m.

**Mom! You're home! You're alive! I've been so worried about you! And here you are!**

It's so good to see you, Raika! How's Lyra? Did she keep you company while I was gone?

**She's fine. I kept a close eye on her. Ridiculously optimistic dog. Nothing but a Golden Retriever in a Belgian Tervuren suit. But enough about her, let's talk about me. I was starting to give up hope that you would ever return, and here you are!**

Yep, I'm here. I'm very happy to see you, too. I missed you!

**Well, this is just so wonderful! Let's celebrate with a walk!**

We can do that. Just give me a minute to put my suitcase down and then we'll go.

**I've waited this long, I can wait a little longer.**

2:30 p.m.

**So good to have you back, Mom! Is it about time for our celebratory walk?**

Pretty soon.

3:00 *p.m.*

**I'm so glad you're home!**

Yes, here I am. Still. I'm definitely home now. Not leaving for a while.

**Well, I am delighted to hear that! How about that celebratory walk that we agreed to over an hour ago?**

Would you like to go now?

**Right now? Good idea!**

It's hot out, but we can go if you really want to.

**I want to!**

9:00 *p.m.*

**It's so perfect! You're still here!**

Yes, Raika, I am. Nice and safe. Trying to go to sleep.

**You even look the same as before you left. Not as though you were in a coma, or dead, or buried, or anything like that.**

Raika, I was not buried, nor in a coma, nor anything else of the kind. I was just traveling for work. Today is my first day back, and I am really, really tired, and I need to sleep. Okay?

**Of course. Did I wake you? Sorry. I was just checking on you.**

That's fine. Now you can stop checking on me. I'm going to sleep now. You can sleep, too.

## 9:30 p.m.

**You're still doing great, Mom. I can tell that you're still breathing.**

There wasn't much question about that. Seriously, Raika. Let me sleep. I'm fine.

**Yes, go ahead! Continue sleeping!**

I can't. You keep waking me up.

**You don't need to wake up when I check on you. I'm just making sure you're getting enough oxygen, blood circulating, all functions normal.**

I'm getting plenty of oxygen.

## 10:00 p.m.

Raika, look. I'm home. I'm fine. Every time you get up and check on me, all of the other dogs think we're getting up. Then Lyra starts running around the room, and Brito walks all over me. I desperately want to sleep now.

**I understand. I'll check very, very quietly from now on. So you just go back to sleep now.**

How about if you don't check at all?

**But what if something happened while you were lying there? I hate to be gruesome, but when you sleep, you look dead.**

I'm not dead. I am very much alive. Just sleeping. I haven't slept well in days, so please? Let me sleep.

**I'll try.**

**11:00 *p.m.***

Oh my god, Raika. Stop!

> **Stopping right now. Just about to go to sleep.**

You are going to be the death of me.

> **What a horrible thing to say at a time like this!**

You have to stop.

**7:00 a.*m.***

> **You did great all night!**

Thank you for letting me sleep.

> **You got better and better! After a while, you stopped waking up when I checked. And here you are.**

Here I am.

> **Maybe a celebratory walk for making it through an entire night?**

No problem. In a little while.

> **Sure. How about breakfast first? Breakfast is due right about now anyway.**

I'm getting up.

> **Good idea! Glad to see your brain is working so well, under the circumstances. I'll tell you though, you've really got to stop traveling. I'm too old to be checking on you all night; I need to be getting my sleep!**

I was thinking you're doing pretty well most days.

> **Let's not take that for granted. Ease up on the travel,**

**okay?**

I'll try.  I want to be here, too.

# Chapter 15:
## Happy Birthday, Raika!

## Raika & Mom

**Happy birthday to me!  Snack, please.**

Here's one.

**Happy birthday to me!  Snack, please.**

And another.

**Happy birthday, dear Raika!  Snack, please.**

One more.

**Happy birthday to me!  Snack, please.**

There you go.  Are you having a good birthday?

**I am!  Walk, please.**

Sure.  Now what?

**Snack, please.**

Coming right up.  Now what?

**Ride up the driveway after my walk.  Plus a snack.  Please.**

No ride up the driveway.  We have to keep your butt in shape!

**Oh, my butt is definitely in shape.  I have never seen another fourteen-year-old dog with a butt like mine.  And today I'm fourteen!  Snack please.**

One snack, a walk up the drive, and… now what?

**Swim, please!**

Can the other dogs come along?  Your choice.

**Hmm... Yes, they can come.**

That's generous of you. They will be pleased.

**I'm in a giving mood. Maybe. Snack, please. But don't give them a snack - a swim is sufficient.**

Later...

So Raika, maybe now a little nap for you so I can get some work done?

**How about a nap for me so you can start making my dinner. Work later. Duck and cherries, right?**

Yes, I'll cook up the duck breast and add the liver and giblets and cherries.

**Wake me when dinner's ready. I'm feeling like a little nap right now.**

Later...

It's done. But it's too hot to eat. What should we do while we wait?

**I think a quick walk. Plus a snack to tide me over. Please.**

Sounds good.

Later...

Your dinner is ready. I put it in your food toy.

**Perfect. Plus I'll clean out the cooking pot. Please.**

Sure. Now what?

**I'm going to shred some paper from the wastebasket, and then rest, and then it will be time for both of us to go to**

**bed. After my ten pieces of bedtime snack. Okay?**

Yes, that's okay. Happy birthday. Glad we're here together. Have I told you how much I love you recently? I do, you know.

**I love you, too! And I have a question.**

What's that?

**Tomorrow, is it over? My birthday?**

Yes. But I put the leftover cooked duck in the freezer, and of course we'll keep walking and swimming, at least until summer is over. Then we'll walk but no more swims.

**Being as I have reached the thoroughly esteemed age of fourteen, what are your thoughts on proceeding to half-yearly birthdays? As we both know, I am fit and shockingly healthy - truly a wonder to behold! And, as we both know, that will not last forever, even if it is the amazing me under consideration. So I'm thinking frequent birthdays are in order now.**

I'm 100% on board with that, and really, you have no idea how happy it makes me to see you doing so well.

**Excellent! And how about the snacks? Maybe a few more throughout the day?**

We really need to cut back on the snacks. We just wrapped up your diet.

**I don't want to push the matter since I've noticed that sometimes humans get rather stuck in their position when they are questioned, but if you take another look at the calendar and do some math, you will see that I have absolutely no time to get fat. Old dogs don't have a fat problem, they have a thin problem. They lose weight and end up practically skeletons. Admittedly, the ten pounds last year was an issue so I'm not faulting your decision there, but be careful about your choices in the future,**

**unless your goal is to have me hit the crematorium as thin as possible - maybe to save on those final expenses? Anyway, I would like to suggest thinking in moderation. Moderate those snacks - all day long. A snack snack here, and a snack snack there, here a snack, there a snack, everywhere a snack snack...**

You're certainly on a roll today - good to see you enjoying your food along with some lively conversation. Some older dogs start to lose their appetites and many have practically nothing to say at all.

**Not this older dog. So are you on board with a frequently-provided and well-moderated string of snacks to help me keep up my strength, lest adversity rear its ugly head, only to stop me cold in my tracks?**

There will be snacks. Just not all the snacks. Okay?

**Just checking the parameters of our relationship on this momentous day! I do appreciate the clarity. Would this be a good time to discuss your travel schedule?**

That topic may be better suited for a different day, but I'm home right now and ever so glad to be here with you.

## Chapter 16:
### Ice Cream Cures Toe Cancer

## Raika & Mom

**Hi, Mom!**

Hi, Raika.

**Lovely afternoon!**

Yes, it's very pretty outside. Why are you so chipper?

**Because you left the open container of training treats on the floor in the bedroom after you trained Lyra, and I ate them.**

Tell me you're lying.

**Nope. I'd lie in a heartbeat if I had a reason, but in this case, why would I? They're gone already, so you can't take them away. Big box, too! And the top was wide open.**

Did you eat ALL of them, or did the other dogs get some, too?

**I ate them all.**

I'm seriously irritated, Raika.

**Sure looks like it! But no reason to take it out on me.**

Yes, there is; you ate all the treats!

**Since when am I not allowed to eat food that I find on the floor in the house? Unlike the exceptionally delicious and well-aged morsels that I find scattered around on our walks, these are free of bacteria! It's not like I took it off the table, though I'd probably do that, too, if I thought I could get away with it. This wasn't even an issue of impulse control. You simply forgot to pick up the box**

**of treats. And while you may well be mad at yourself, that is no justification for redirecting your anger at me. Or anyway, that's what you would tell the kids if they were angry at you for something foolish they had done themselves. So the solution is that you must accept your error and move on! Besides, you weren't very nice to me earlier, so maybe this is payback of sorts.**

Really? I thought you had a good day. A swim to cool you off followed up by a walk and, apparently, an entire box of dog treats. Where did I err this time?

**Besides your tone, which I will ignore, you "erred" in the pool-related part of my day.**

What did I do wrong?

**My white toy is at the bottom of the deep end of the pool where I cannot reach it anymore. I wanted it, and you knew that. You ignored my distress and just stood there, watching.**

Ah. Well, yes, I noticed that you were standing in the water, but since my primary interest was getting you good and wet for your walk, things were going fine from my point of view. Also, I did throw the orange toy for you several times, thinking you might go for that instead and forget about the white one.

**And how likely was that? You know I have an obsessive personality. Taunting me with another toy at a time like that isn't very considerate.**

I suppose not. I did see that you ignored the orange one. But at least Lyra was happy! She played with the orange toy the whole time we were out there!

**I see no positive correlation between Lyra's happiness and mine. In fact, there may even be an inverse relationship between Lyra's happiness and mine. And anyway, right now, we're talking about me. I think we need to make this**

**situation right.**

How's that?

**Get the white toy off the bottom for me and pour the water out of it so that it sinks very, very slowly so that I can dive for it before it hits the bottom. Such an amazingly satisfying thing to do in the pool - I can't believe more dogs don't take up diving for a hobby! Now, if we did that, if you fetched that toy back up and we used it for diving practice? Then we could have a second try at our day, and maybe you can get it right this time.**

Maybe later, okay?

**Later is fine. I will stand here by the door, staring at the pool, and practicing a non-stop, low-level whine while you figure out exactly what "later" means to you.**

(Indecipherable mumbling.)

**I heard that.**

What did you hear, Raika?

**That "Raika-is-a-lot-of-trouble-these-days" bit you just mumbled under your breath.**

That just slipped out. I didn't actually mean it - even though I guess I did. How about if we dredge your toy off the pool bottom and have a second swim complete with a diving session right now?

**Fantastic! Probably a good thing I ate those treats earlier; a little fuel never hurts an athlete like me. What about the other dogs? Can they stay in the house and scream at the windows while I play? That really does add considerably to the overall experience.**

No. They're coming along.

## Mom & Raika

You ate fast this morning; glad to see you enjoying your meal!

**Yep. I enjoyed my breakfast and all is well. Can I have a little more, please?**

I don't think so. Remember the diet we just finished? That was brutal, and we don't want to go through it again.

**Mom, didn't we just discuss this recently? In what alternate universe is a fourteen-year-old dog in danger of getting fat enough to require another round of dieting?**

In the universe we're in right now - you know, the one where you're doing amazingly well and might live several more years.

**Since you seem to be obsessed with matters of health and longevity... I have a little pain in my foot.**

What? Where? I don't see anything.

**It's there. A serving of ice cream would probably help.**

What has ice cream got to do with your foot?

**The cold numbs the pain. Furthermore, if I'm on the verge of death's door from toe cancer, what difference does it make?**

What are you talking about? Unless you stick your foot in the ice cream, it's not going to numb anything. Plus, I've never heard of toe cancer.

**Toe cancer is a terrible thing, if somewhat rare.**

Are you limping?

**Yes. It's quite painful, I tell you.**

You showed me the left foot a minute ago, and now you're holding up the other one.

**Wow! It's already metastasizing.**

Raika, I have begun to think you're just making this up to get ice cream.

**It was worth a shot. So… how about a bit of ice cream for your old dog who won't be here forever?**

I should have seen that coming.

**You're absolutely right that it makes no sense to stick my foot in the ice cream and waste a perfectly good snack. But the pool is another matter altogether. We could follow that ice cream up with a cool swim for a sore toe.**

Yesterday when we went swimming, you refused to get out of the pool when it was time. I don't have time for your shenanigans today; I have to get some work done.

**I wasn't refusing. I was waiting until you got my toy. You left it sitting on the bottom at the end of my swim, and experience has taught me that you're not all that reliable about getting it back for me unless I take notable measures to get your attention.**

Why does that matter? The toy can stay on the bottom till the end of days and nothing will happen to it. But it's pretty annoying when you paddle around in circles just out of reach.

**I had to stay out of reach or you might have hauled me out of the water.**

That's exactly the point! And since I let you swim before we even went for our walk AND I allowed for a bonus swim afterward, I thought that was pretty obnoxious. It was a hundred degrees out there, not a good time for your games.

**I know! It was beyond hot! That's why I stayed in the water. The water was nice. Plus – my toy. You should**

**have gotten into the water, too. Life is short, so swim a
little! Then you could have easily gotten my toy.**

If you do that again, I'm not going to take you swimming when we
come home from our walks. I have to get some work done, and I
can't spend all my time begging you to get out of the water.

**Did you try food?**

Food?

**Yes. You should have gone to the kitchen, grabbed
something tasty like the bowl of ice cream I am currently
requesting, and bribed me. I might have come if it was
good enough.**

Since when do I do things like that?

**With my hearing loss, for all we know, I couldn't even
hear you when you were calling me. But if you had waved
a bowl of ice cream around, I would have noticed that.
Oh! Or those duck and cherry treats with the crunchy
texture? Those are truly amazing - a culinary delight for
sure. Speaking of treats, we're running low on duck and
cherry treats.**

How do you know that?

**I looked earlier today.**

How can you look? They're on the back of the counter.

**I just put my feet up and took a quick peek.**

Raika, I put them up high for a reason. You shouldn't be putting your
feet up on the counter. That's bad manners. Plus you're setting a bad
example for the other dogs.

**The other dogs are not entering the home stretch, so that's
like comparing apples and oranges. I was checking on
our supplies. It's a good thing, too! It's time to reorder.**

**Maybe even set up one of those recurring shipment plans? Then we wouldn't have to worry about it.**

For now, we have some other treats. They're not your favorite, but they'll do until the next time I'm shopping. Then I'll get some more of the duck and cherry ones.

**Ten, nine, eight...**

Why are you counting down?

**Musing on the frail timeline of life.**

You are not going to die in the next ten days.

**Who said days? Could be weeks, months - who knows? Maybe I'll be a record holder, and it will be years! Isn't that the point? No one really knows.**

I'm shopping tomorrow. That's soon enough, isn't it?

**I may have just hours. Could be ten hours.**

Enough of the doom and gloom.

**Minutes! It could be minutes!**

Raika, stop changing the conversation. We're talking about getting out of the pool, not ordering more of your preferred treats. Just get out of the pool when it's time, okay?

**I hear you. I'll think about it.**

Raika & Mom

**Mom, what was up with the extra people around?**

Friends came over for a little pool party.

**They don't have dogs.**

What makes you think that?

**They put food on the coffee table at muzzle height and then turned away to talk to their friends. Very thoughtful, really. Padded my breakfast nicely. Who doesn't enjoy a good game of "outwit the human"? Although, admittedly, it's not very sporting when I take the sandwich right in front of them and they barely look over. More like shooting fish in a barrel than using my wit. Now, when Nick's friends come over, that's when I have a chance to use my wit.**

You're not supposed to take the food just because you can. At your age, you should know better than that.

**Au contraire! That is exactly why I'm supposed to take it; I'm now plenty old enough to be operating under old dog rules. Plus, your guests just go make more, so no one goes home hungry. I have no real desire to be a human, but I do admire your opposable thumbs.**

I think eating those random foods might be contributing to some of your nighttime tummy troubles. You must have been up five times last night.

**Oh, I don't think that was because of your pool party. It's more likely that came from Nick's friends.**

Raika, what do you mean?

**I was hanging out with Nick's guests in the evening. After your friends went home. I think their food is more likely to contribute to tummy troubles. Rich and greasy and devoid of nutrition, you know?**

Again? Damn. I told them not to leave food on the coffee table. How did you make it happen this time?

**As I said, I was using my wit! In a nutshell, being cute–old and a bit doddering pays off huge dividends when one wants to acquire some French fries. That's what they were eating, you know. French fries.**

How many French fries did you get?

**Well I didn't count them individually, but there were five boys, five packs of French fries, and I'm pretty sure I got more than one pack's worth. The trick is to tailor your approach to each individual. Gently tap this one on the ankle with your foot, that one in the corner does better with a chin on his thigh, and one in particular was a total sucker for my milky blue eyes. These cataracts are serving me well. Nothing like a milky-blue-eyed stare to get a second French fry from a greedy child. I am old, you know.**

Your age came up?

**Absolutely. Anytime there was a hint of withholding, Nick would remind them. "She's fourteen! Give her the French fry!" Nick really is a very fine advocate.**

Raika, I worry about your tummy with all of these random foods. You were up and down several times last night. I think I need to chat with your advocate; I already told him not to let his friends give you extra food.

**I assume Dad got up each time to let me out, so no worries there.**

Assume? Don't you remember?

**Nope, not a thing. More restful that way.**

It worries me that you're doing things at night and not remembering them the next day. I'll mention it to the vet. I think it might be getting a little worse.

**The vet is not the least bit interested in my nocturnal activities, so feel free to skip that conversation. Besides, I don't mind getting up a few extra times at night in exchange for a veritable banquet of culinary options during the day!**

Maybe it's working for you, but Dad and I need some sleep, too. So if we can solve it, I'd like to figure it out. It's weird-old.

**French fries and a few nocturnal adventures aren't going to hurt me any.**

Sure, all things in moderation, but my point was about you not remembering, not the French fries or what you actually do at night.

**I was absolutely moderate. No more than one pack of French fries for Raika. Well, maybe two. You know, I might have to start the blue-eyed stare with you. Don't you think my eyes are particularly irresistible?**

Raika? You're changing the topic. What are we going to do about your sleeping problem?

**We don't have a problem.**

I disagree. We have a problem.

**Well, you're the dog trainer. Go ahead and solve it.**

## Chapter 17:
## Much Ado About Nothing

### Raika & Mom

**Much ado about nothing, if you ask me.**

Raika, how can you say that? I've been trying to get Brito in the pool for four years.

**You had to pick him up and hold him on the step!**

Be a little more charitable. He was asking me to pick him up and put him on the step.

**The water is only four inches deep on the step.**

It's a big deal to go from one inch of water in his kiddie pool to four inches in the big pool.

**I never needed my own kiddie pool. I went straight to the big pool!**

You were a much bigger dog. It made sense to get Brito a little pool to help him out.

**He fell in! He didn't want to go!**

He only sort of fell in because he was thinking so hard about jumping.

**I watched it happen. He went to the edge, tripped, and by the grace of God, he landed on the step with his feet under him.**

And then he learned from it!

**No, he didn't. He didn't jump in next. You and Dad had to talk him into it. You had to make sure that he went in at exactly the right place or he would have face-planted**

**and gone straight to the bottom.**

That's why I need to get him a little life jacket. That way, if he misses the step, he won't get scared. Way too early for him to practice diving.

**I never needed a life jacket.**

Look, we're all good at different things. You should congratulate him on his bravery.

**When he swims his first lap without a life jacket, I'll congratulate him.**

Are you, perhaps, just a little jealous of how much attention he got for his first swim? Everyone cheering him on and all?

**Swim?! You call tripping into the pool and escaping three seconds later a swim?**

A lot jealous?

**I'm not jealous. You have no sense of priorities. Did you happen to videotape any of my spectacular dives to the bottom of the pool, or were you too busy on your phone? Those dives are something to get excited about! Remember when I was younger and I could do that in the deep end? Wow! Amazing stuff for sure right there. And I can still do the middle of the pool, full of style! I should have gone out for the Olympic team.**

Amazing for sure, Raika. And at some point we need to talk about your diving. You come up sputtering a whole lot more often lately. You're getting a little older, and I'm wondering if it might be time to start cutting back...

**My favorite dives are when you toss that toy in and then we wait, watching as it gets lower and lower in the water. And then, just before it looks absolutely impossible - boom! Off I go, slicing through the water like a seabird after a fish! But that toy has no chance against the**

**amazing diving Raika because I have carefully calculated each of my moves to ensure another successful score.**

Maybe this is not the best day for this conversation.

## Raika & Mom

**Mom? Just wanted to mention that I enjoyed Brito's last swimming lesson immensely!**

That's great! I'm glad you like watching him swim. I do, too!

**The Brito swimming part was okay, but that's not what I was paying attention to. The best part of the lesson was when you re-enacted the various parts of that classic Far Side cartoon.**

Which Far Side cartoon?

**The one where the person is telling the dog to lie down, but the dog doesn't do it, so the guy keeps scrunching closer and closer to the ground until he's lying down, but the dog is still standing. Do you know that one? It's one of my favorites!**

Oh, yeah. I've seen that one.

**When you started the lesson, both of you were out of the water. Next, you were on the first step and Brito was out of the water. Then, you were on the second step, and then the third one. Finally, you were all the way in the pool, still wearing all of your clothes! And where was Brito? Running back and forth along the edge of the pool! Lyra and I agreed that the odds were maybe fifty-fifty that he would jump in the water for you. No go, I see.**

He was so close!

**It was better this way. First-class entertainment.**

Glad we were able to entertain you. Next time I hope he just jumps in.

**This was so much better. Hysterical!**

Gee, thanks for all the support.

**For sure. You know what's not so funny?**

What?

**The suitcase you pulled out. Are you traveling again? Didn't you learn anything from your recent close call?**

It's okay, Raika. I won't be gone very long. I'll be back in a week.

**Where are you going?**

Austria.

**What's going to happen to me?**

Nothing is going to "happen" to you, Raika. You know Dad takes good care of you when I'm gone.

**That's fine for a few days, but what if you don't come back?**

Years, Raika. For years you've watched me travel. I go, I'm gone a short while, and then I come back. I have always come back.

**What if I die while you're gone? Some days aren't so great anymore. You know that; we've both seen some changes these past few months. I would hate for you to be gone if I got sick or something.**

I'll be honest, I do worry about you when I'm gone. I'm trying to travel less - I really am. I want to be home with you, especially now that you're getting older. Maybe when I get back, we can talk about your sleeping patterns. I feel like you've been ignoring that whole thing, and I don't really know if it means anything or not.

**I just want you to be home with me.**

I promise you I'm working on it. But not yet. I scheduled some engagements a while ago and I can't get out of them now. But I am absolutely working on cutting back.

**Yeah. Well. I wish you'd just stay home.**

# Part Two

# Chapter 18:
## Abandoned after a Life of Selfless Service

## Raika & Lyra

**It's time for us to face the cold, hard reality. She's not coming back. This is really it.**

Raika, you're exasperating! She comes back every time!

**We've been through this before. The past does not guarantee the future. She's been gone long enough that if she planned to return, she would have done so by now.**

Maybe you should try to distract yourself.

**With what? Dad already took us swimming, and now he's not even home. Really, if you think about it, he could be getting hit by a car and killed right now, even as we speak. Then no one will come back to take care of us, and we'll die for sure if the kids end up in charge. They won't even remember to feed us, never mind details like swimming or bedtime stories. I think I'll start working on my obituary. I'm not going to bother with a will - you'll be dead, too.**

**Raika**

**May 2004 - August 2018**

**Abandoned after a life of selfless service.**

Does this mean you would have given us your stuff if we survived?

**Not necessarily. It just means I don't even have to consider the possibility. I'm not sure I'll want to share, even after I'm dead.**

She'll be back, and then the issue of your stuff won't even come up.

**Hmph.**

You'll see... So anyway, Raika, why do you wander around the house at night? Mom is worried about that for sure.

**I don't understand this obsession everyone has over my sleep - I get enough sleep. And while my memory is not always perfect, it's good enough.**

Raika? Your memory issues are pretty weird.

**Shut up, Lyra. Everyone around here wants to make a mountain out of a molehill.**

## Raika & Mom

**And here you are, Mom!**

Here I am!

**I'm impressed at how you keep doing that.**

Doing what?

**Coming back. Just when you're on the brink of being gone forever, you pull that old rabbit out of a hat.**

At some point, shouldn't that trick get predictable?

**Impresses me every time.**

I see.

**What's on the agenda for today?**

I have a little catching up to do around here, and then for sure a walk with you. Have you noticed it's getting colder now? Looks like we're in for a change of season.

**But it's not too cold to swim, right?**

Definitely not too cold to swim. We'll do that in the afternoon.

**Good. Nice to have you back!**

Nice to be here.

**Moving on to another topic... I'm going to start working on being polite, and of course I wanted you to be the first to know. As they say, I'm turning over a new leaf!**

I think that's a fantastic idea!

**Yes, and I have a request. I would like you to find my white swimming toy before we swim today. Please.**

Your white swimming toy? Have you noticed your orange toy? It's in the pool area right now. We could go and play with it!

**Yes, I know all about the orange one. I want the white one. Please! Are you noticing my excellent manners?**

I am noticing your excellent manners. And I really appreciate them. That's why it occurs to me that we could go swimming right now rather than waiting for the afternoon.

**That would be lovely. And the color of the toy that we will play with - will it be white? Please!**

I'm pretty sure it will be orange. But it's a really great toy. Just like the white one, but without a hole in it.

**But that is exactly the problem! I want a hole in it. First it gets thrown in the pool. Then I watch it sink. Then I dive to the bottom and retrieve it. The hole is why I want it. Please!**

Raika, I have some concerns about that toy. I don't like the way it sinks. As often as not, you push it into the deep end, and I don't like the way you look when you dive for it. I'm concerned that you're pushing yourself too hard, and that in your enthusiasm for getting the toy, you might stay underwater for too long. It would be terrible if you took in a big breath of water. I tried to talk to you about it recently, but you kept changing the topic.

**Mom, I've been diving for toys for years. Have I ever inhaled water? No. I know what I'm doing! Besides, wouldn't you jump in and save me?**

You're very talented! But I'm not sure that you're as strong as you used to be. And of course I would go in and fish you out, but that would be like scooping you up off the street after you'd been hit by a car. It would be too late, and you could end up very sick.

**Why don't we throw the sinking toy just for today and see how I do? Please?**

Because what if today is the day that you end up with a lungful of water?

**The absolute best part of swimming is diving for my toy. I don't want the orange one. You've seen what happens when you throw the orange one: it floats. I know the white one is around somewhere. Please?**

Since the white one always sinks, I thought it was a good idea to get rid of it.

**Tell me you didn't throw it away. Did you? Please, no. Are you still noticing all of my nice pleases?**

I have noticed all of your nice pleases! But the most important thing to me is your safety. I'm not saying you're old. I'm saying your rear isn't quite as strong as it has been in the past.

**How is that different than saying I'm old? Am I going to get stronger? Will my toy come back? Please?**

Let me think about this some more. Maybe there's a solution. Can we talk about it later?

**Yes... Okay, it's later. What are you thinking?**

I didn't mean thirty seconds later. I meant a day or two so I can have a chat with Dad, weigh the pros and cons - you know. Think about it.

**I'm old! We don't have time for all that thinking! Let's hear your idea now. Please!**

How about if we tie your white toy to your orange toy, so it doesn't sink to the bottom?

**But it wouldn't sink then?**

It will sink! Just not to the bottom.

**So it won't sink?**

You're being difficult. It will absolutely, definitely sink - about two feet, I think. So you can play all of the parts of your game: watch it fall, think about it, bark a little, target it, and boom! Hit it like a diving bird catching a fish!

**But what about the adventure part? The part where I think I might be going too far underwater, and maybe I can do it, but maybe not? So I have to strategize. Then, when the suspense can grow no greater - splash! In I go! It's a mental toughness exercise, you know. The adrenaline of possibility! Let's stay with what we have now. Please!**

I'm trying to compromise here. What is your contribution to this conversation?

**I suggest that we keep on the way we were before. If I forget to keep the sinking toy in the shallow end, and if it goes too deep before I dive, then you can fish it out with the net. If it would please you, of course.**

That would be a bit of a chore since I'm trying to keep an eye on the other dogs, too. I have to throw their toys and make sure they're busy, as well.

**So Lyra and Brito can't wait for ten seconds while you pull your faithful old companion's toy into the shallow end so that she can maintain her physical and mental fitness without drowning? Also, I noticed you left your trusty**

**companion cell phone out of this conversation as well. You might need to put that down and pay more attention to what is happening around you - or is that the straw that broke the camel's back when it comes to supervising me?**

As soon as the words were out of my mouth, I knew I had made a mistake.

**Indeed. So let's go with the second option. You put your phone down and keep an eye on my sinking toy. If it goes more than a few feet, then you get the net and scoop it into shallower water while the other dogs wait patiently. Or impatiently - that's not really important. Please!**

We'll try that.

**So. Did my fantastically great manners influence this conversation in any way?**

You started off strong, but then I thought you were trying to manipulate me.

**That transparent? Maybe this is not the style for me.**

Are you admitting that you were trying to manipulate me?

**Well, in a nutshell, yes.**

So Raika. Maybe go with the "honesty is the best policy" approach instead - just lay it out there like it is, and when you get called on it, you can say you were just being honest.

**Certainly closer to my personality. Plus it might do you some good; I can open your mind to the truth, even the uncomfortable ones! Or something like that.**

Yes. Something like that!

**I will enjoy this shift in direction. The politeness thing is time-consuming and hard to remember! I'm going to sit down and work on my new strategy.**

## Chapter 19:
### Humans Must Not Eat the Dog Treats

### Raika & Mom

**I hope you're feeling bad about mistreating me. It was a hot day and the pool was right there. How am I supposed to keep up my fitness if we don't swim?!**

Raika, I took you for a long walk early in the morning when it was cool. Doesn't that count?

**That was a long time ago. Maybe it wasn't even today - maybe it was yesterday? I get confused about my days sometimes. And my most vivid memory of that walk was the rate at which you consumed those peanut butter pretzels in your pocket. Those aren't for adults! Those are for kids and dogs!**

Are we talking about swimming or walking or eating?

**Talking about walking reminded me of eating. Talking about eating reminded me of pretzels, and that reminded me that you were eating my pretzels on our walk!**

Raika, adults eat peanut butter pretzels all the time. I find them convenient for dog treats, so I give them to you as well.

**I'm not comfortable with you reaching into the dog treat pocket and then sticking something in your mouth. That seems wrong. I mean, what if we ran low? We could be walking along and boom! Out of nowhere, the big one comes! We could be trapped there on the trail for days before anyone found us. And I would have no snacks. I'm feeling a little sick with the possibility of it all.**

If that happens, we'll be sharing your snacks regardless of what they are or who they were originally intended for. As a matter of fact, that reminds me of a book I read. This guy and his dog got stuck on a trail and he was starving, so he ate his dog.

**What a terrible story! Why would you tell me a thing like that?!**

You're right. It just popped in my head and I decided to share it with you. That was not appropriate, but don't worry, I'm not going to eat you.

**So now on top of being hungry on account of watching you eat my snacks, I'm going to have nightmares. It's like you were raised in a barn.**

I promise I'll never eat you. And the pretzel thing - it was just mindless eating while we were walking. There was plenty for you as well.

**Well, next time we come across a rotting carcass, I'm going to mindlessly eat it before you have a chance to stop me. Of course, there's plenty for you as well.**

Now you're being irritable. Regardless, the walk was definitely today. This morning. And the walk was instead of a swim. I took you out early so you'd be comfortable. It's a little late to swim now, don't you think? We've already had dinner. We should take another look at this in the morning. Maybe tomorrow afternoon would be just right for a swim.

**Feeling guilt now?**

Raika, sometimes I have to fish you out of the pool when you get obstinate, so swimming after dinner is a questionable idea.

**I promise not to be obstinate, okay? I'll get out after a reasonable amount of time. If you want to help me remember my promise, bring a toy so you can snag it with the pool net if you need to.**

Fine. With great trepidation, we'll do it.

**Great word, Mom: trepidation!**

If you want to work on your vocabulary, check out "incorrigible."

**I already know that one. Any reason you're asking?**

Never mind. Let's go ahead and swim.

# Part Two

# Chapter 20:
## The Complicated World of Human Behavior

### Raika & Mom

**I couldn't help but notice that you are reading an article about dogs who can count.**

Fascinating stuff, Raika. People didn't realize until now that dogs could count, and I think that's pretty amazing. I figured I would read the article while I wait for our dinner to cool. Dad cooked a pot roast and asked me to keep an eye on it while he made a phone call in his office.

**That's kind of like Columbus "discovering" America. The Native Americans knew all about it... I can count, you know.**

I didn't know that, Raika.

**Yep. I can. For example, today I counted that Lyra had three training sessions, Brito had two, and I had zip. None. Nada. Notice that I can also speak a foreign language.**

I think you should stop spending so much time worrying about what the other dogs might have gotten that you didn't.

**That is totally unrealistic. I need to pay close attention to ensure my fair share - plus a touch more.**

Between what you are given, what you take from the other dogs against their will, and what you scavenge in spite of my attempts to stop you, I'm quite sure that you are getting your fair share plus quite a lot more.

**That's one perspective. When you finish up that article, you might want to head back to your computer and see if they've started teaching dogs to read, too; now that would**

**be interesting!**

Unfortunately, I can't leave the kitchen right now. I don't trust you with our dinner, and I promised Dad I'd stay here until he got back.

**You don't trust me? Have you no heart? You go right for the emotional jugular of your faithful companion of all these years?**

I have a heart. I also have a brain, and I don't like the way you're staring at the counter where dinner is cooling, so I'm keeping an eye on you.

**Whatever happened to seeing the good in others?**

Not you, Raika. You've gone rogue. The whole family knows it.

**What a thing to say!**

Raika, lately the only time you're not getting into trouble is when you're on your walk. And now that I think about it, you make mischief there as well.

**What mischief?**

Well, today it was the food you found. I don't even know what it was - leftovers of something.

**The ham sandwich?**

How would I know? I saw you zeroing in on a target, but I didn't even try to call you back because I knew it was a lost cause. You finished it before I got close enough to see what it was.

**Yeah, that was a ham sandwich. You know, the deli kind, with lots of slices of thin meat all folded in waves so it looks extra-thick and appealing? It was good. A little dirty, but never mind that. Can you imagine how a sandwich of that quality ended up there on the trail? Some person lovingly made it and the recipient just dumped the leftovers!**

Maybe he was trying to feed the homeless animals, Raika. Which you are not.

> **I don't know what has gotten into you. I'm finding you irritable and judgmental lately. Do we have friends that can help you with that? Maybe you should stop reading so much about dogs and consider the self-help options instead.**

I will ignore that and get back to my work.

> **Does that mean you're going to stop babysitting the dinner that is sitting near the edge of the counter, about six inches back and over from the stove?**

Thanks for the reminder! Looks like it's cool enough to eat now.

> **Are you interested in sharing?**

Let's see what's left after the family eats.

> **I thought I was family?**

The human family.

> **Oh. Well, if anyone should get too full, you know you could give me whatever is left on that person's plate. Or if you should notice that your pants are feeling a bit tight, you could even quit before you were full and benefit both of us.**

Thoughtful as ever, Raika.

## Raika & Mom

> **Walk time!**

How about later, Raika? I'm tired.

> **Ah. Okay. Then why don't you get off your computer, take a little nap, and we'll go when you wake up. I'm not**

**sure what all you went through these past months.**

Raika, I didn't "go through" anything. I just traveled on occasion.

**Sure. That's fine. Sometimes it's better to repress the details. So go take your nap and we'll walk later. Or check with Dad; is he available to take me out?**

I don't take naps and Dad isn't home right now.

**Well, how will you stop being tired if you don't take a nap? Are you just going to magically stop being tired?**

To be honest, it's not so much that I'm tired. I just don't want to go for a walk right now.

**Why didn't you say so? How can I possibly give you good advice if I don't know what the problem is?**

"I'm tired" is just an expression. It can also mean that I'm not in the mood for whatever someone else is proposing.

**In the complicated world of human behavior, I would suggest that obfuscation is not a winner. Why would a person choose to use an expression that clearly has a different meaning from what they are really feeling? Or maybe you just don't want to admit that you like working more than walking with me?**

Because a vague phrase like that is often easier than explaining what we really think or feel.

**I honestly don't know how your species has survived as long as they have. How can you possibly communicate when you misrepresent your state of mind like that? Here you are, the only species who can carry on random chats over all manner of things, and you opt to lie about the simplest matters.**

People don't necessarily want to expose their true feelings. If I say I'm tired, others simply accept it. If I say I love working more than walking, then I feel bad just hearing the words.

**Dogs are much simpler. If I'm happy, you know I'm happy. If I'm sad, you know I'm sad. And if I'm angry, you'll know that too. Right now, I can feel sadness and anger building.**

Which one is it, Raika? Sad or angry?

**Hmmm. When we started this conversation, I was gradually getting angry, mostly because I learned that you were lying to me. But now I'm getting sad because I don't think I'm going to get my walk. I think you're going to keep typing away on that computer.**

I changed my mind, Raika. I think we should go for a walk right now. I need to get out.

**Well, now I'm happy! Let's go before you get tired or sad or an urgent email comes through or whatever else you might randomly come up with. Plus, it's getting hot out there.**

## Mom

If ever a living being has figured out how to turn back the hands of time, it's Raika. Yes, her eyes are a bit cloudy and she has some arthritis. And yes, I know that it's time to address some of her more reckless activities - for example, the diving has to stop. But at the age of 14, what dog doesn't have some concerns to address?

So how am I to reconcile what I see in front of me with the calendar on the wall? How am I to make good decisions for us when her very existence seems to belie the rules of time for everyone else?

I had planned to cut my travel schedule back so that I could spend more time with her, but that seems premature given the overall situation. I still see a whole lot of cute-old with very little sick-old on the horizon. Will she be one of those unusual dogs who lives to be 17 or 18 years of age in good health?

As I consider that dream I had not so very long ago, I struggle to feel the fear and panic that forced me awake and caused me to look carefully at her face - to see how much time we might have left. I know that the end is inevitable. Yet, I find myself slipping into the warm cocoon of denial, that cozy space where everything will be okay for eternity. She'll be fine. She's not leaving me, at least not for a very long while, so why worry about it?

Aging is inevitable. I can say it. I can know it. My husband and I can talk about it. But today I cannot feel it. Her life is a gift to me, and I think she may be here for a very long time to come.

# Fall 2018

## Chapter 21:
## The Great Bedtime Debacle

### Mom & Raika

Raika, why are you following me around the house? Do you really think that I cannot manage a trip to the kitchen and back without supervision?

> **One can never be too careful! What if you opened the refrigerator door and accidentally hit yourself on the head? Or what if the knife slipped and you sliced open your hand while you were trying to cut a piece of cheese for a sandwich?**

Are either of those scenarios likely?

> **I've noticed that you're not very good with safety details.**

Okay, so that explains the kitchen. Why do you follow me into the bathroom? Do you think there is some particular danger in there, as well?

> **Are you crazy?! The bathroom is extremely dangerous! Did you know that the bathroom is the most common place for a person to have a heart attack?**

I did not know that.

> **Totally true. And if you were to have a heart attack and die because nobody knew you were there, I would never forgive myself.**

Well, that's kind of sweet, Raika. Thank you for that.

**It's possible there is some self-interest involved, but sure, let's go with it and say it's 100% altruistic.**

Not everything has to be said out loud, right?

**That's what I was thinking, too. I've always liked your expression, "Not every thought that enters your head needs to come out of your mouth."**

I try to remember that one. Still a work in progress.

**That's okay. I struggle with that one too, but I am learning to do better. Now that I think about it, isn't there some research that says that dogs learn better when they've had a snack?**

Yes, I think there is.

**I am having a thought right now, but nothing's coming out of my mouth. What might we do to enhance my learning?**

Why don't we go to the kitchen and grab a cookie for you.

**Wow, it worked! Maybe I can keep more thoughts inside my head than I knew.**

Always worth a shot... Ouch! That was my finger!

**Sorry, sorry, sorry! I really didn't see your finger. I thought that was the cookie.**

No, that was most certainly not the cookie. That was my finger. Owie. I don't think you've done that since you were a puppy.

**It was definitely an accident. However, since we're discussing it, where did the cookie go? You don't want it left on the floor, do you?**

It's right here. Where I dropped it when I jerked my hand back.

**Where?**

Here!

**Mom, that's not a cookie; that's simply a vague smell of deliciousness somewhere in the vicinity. I can't see it!**

It's kind of small. Actually, it's one of Brito's cookies.

**That's a Brito cookie? I think this is the first time in my life that I've felt sincerely sorry for the little white dog.**

You're making me feel worse than I already do. He's a little chunky right now. We're trying to cut back before he ends up on a full-on diet like you went through.

**Is that really the best you can do for him?**

I think so.

**Well, rather than dwelling on chunky Brito's misfortunes, could we just have some kind of agreement that you won't try to feed me his treats? Because honestly, Mom, even when my eyes were really good, I'm not sure I could've found a treat like that, and after I ate it, I'd be wondering whether I ate anything or not. I mean, the more I think about it, the less I think this is a function of my eyesight. And seeing as I was getting that snack so that I could practice keeping some of my thoughts in, I think you need to do a little better.**

I'll make sure we use more substantial offerings in the future. Though, Raika? I hate to break it to you, but that mistake would not have happened when you were younger. You would have seen that treat and been very careful about my finger - this shark thing you're doing around food is new. By the way, I've noticed that the unfettered flow of thoughts has re-emerged.

**First, I'd like to point out that I didn't actually eat your finger, which means I'm still looking for that morsel. I'd also like to suggest that holding in thoughts that could lead to my demise via starvation are not suitable for niceties**

like staying silent.  When it's serious, I have an obligation
to speak up, if only to ensure my survival.  Could I have
another, larger, dog treat, please?

## Mom & Raika

Raika, I have some bad news.

I'm sorry to hear that.  But now that we've started our
walk, how about if we wait until we get back home before
we start to stew in negativity?

I need to tell you now because it affects you.

How is that?

I forgot your cookies.

What do you mean?

Well, Raika, you pushed me so hard to get going on our walk that I
just forgot them.

So if I'm hearing you correctly, it's my fault that
you forgot the snacks?  Wow, that's some first-class
rationalization right there.  Classic.  Regardless, let's
double-check.  Both pockets in front?

Raika, really - there are none.

Back pockets?

Same.

How about the back left side.  Did you reach all the way
to the bottom?  The smaller pieces sometimes get jammed
down there.

I can look, Raika, but without a good dose of magic, there just aren't
any treats in my pockets.

Is there someone we can call?  Dad, maybe?  It's about

**time we found a use for that cell phone that benefits me. This is important.**

I think we'll have to do without.

**Without?**

Yes, Raika. Without.

**Well then, there is something that you need to know as well.**

What's that?

**Be prepared to watch me like a hawk; if I have to turn wild to survive, I'll take any opportunities that come my way.**

Turn wild to survive? Is that not perhaps a bit dramatic?

**Let's see what you say when I find that deer carcass that has been aging for over two months now.**

That is completely gone, Raika. They took it away a long time ago.

**Okay.**

What do you mean, "Okay"?

**Just what I said. Okay. We'll go past the deer carcass spot and there won't be anything there, so nothing to worry about when I head in that direction. And come back chewing.**

Raika, do you remember the time you got into the kitchen trash and you ended up with your mouth burning something terrible?

**Yes, it was terrible! But what has that got to do with today's tragedy?**

Well, do you remember that I suggested that the entire misfortune could have been avoided if you would stop taking things out of the kitchen trash - something I had specifically taught you not to do to avoid such a possibility from occurring?

**Yes, I remember.  Why?**

I was going to ask you if you'd learned anything from that event - taking things that I told you not to take.

**I was just about to ask you the same thing!  It's your responsibility to make sure that big chunks of wasabi and ginger don't end up in the trash amongst the good food!**

It was my understanding that things in the wastepaper basket are for you to shred, and things in the kitchen trash are really trash.  I had no idea that I was responsible for preventing you from getting into the kitchen trash so as to avoid another incident, so I told you not to do it anymore.  And now, here I am telling you not to eat dead and rotting things on the road because you'll be sorry, just like you were when you ended up with a mouthful of wasabi and ginger from the trash.

**Here we go, blaming the victim again.  Don't leave the trash out for me to eat!  And if you really don't think I should supplement my diet with whatever I might find, then don't leave the house without my cookies!**

We never even brought cookies on your walks until we went out with Brito and you saw that he got cookies on his walks.  As I recall, you managed just fine.

**And I am forever grateful to the little white guy for that, even as I pity him the crumbs he accepts as having actual food value.**

## Raika & Mom

**I just want you to know that I will remember this as The Great Bedtime Debacle of 2018.**

Raika, wouldn't a debacle be something more severe than running low on bedtime snacks?

**Running low? It's always ten! We count them together: One for me. Two for me. Three for me. One for Lyra. And a crumb for Brito. Then we continue on. Four for me, five for me, and so on. It's always that way! Plus, you didn't remember the most basic part of the routine. You didn't even give me even one!**

I know, Raika. I forgot. I went to bed.

**Well, I saved us there and got you right up. I can't sleep without a snack – I need it or I feel sick. Bedtime is my hungry time!**

That's why I got up. I felt bad that I forgot, and frankly, it was clear that no one was going to get any sleep if you didn't get your snack. I just don't believe that five or ten snacks makes that much of a difference.

**If your paycheck came back cut in half, due to no fault of your own, would you be talking about "not much" of a difference? Yeah, what's one or five or ten when it comes to dollars? And about those snacks, you could have made more. Or called a friend to make them. I bet your friends would have understood the emergency right away and brought them over. They know about emergencies. It's okay to call friends at night when it's an emergency.**

Made them in the middle of the night? You're right - you would've had better luck getting one of my friends to do it than me. I'm amazed I even managed to get out of bed to find you the first five snacks, which is when I discovered we had run out. Couldn't you be grateful for the five?

**There's no chance I could have had a restful night's sleep after that. I couldn't even count snacks in my head to help me sleep, because every time I got to three or four, I would start to get upset – we all know what should happen after five! But there was no six. There was no sixth snack!**

I'll make you a new batch of snacks later today – with peanut butter and cream and other things, too. And, just to show that I am contrite, I will give you extra tonight. Fifteen. Would you like fifteen snack bites?

**I would. But now I'm tired. Been up all night over the injustice of this.**

How about if I give you an afternoon snack right now - a bonus!

**Closer to forgiveness, but afternoon is not my hungry time unless I'm scavenging on a walk. What are you doing right now? Maybe you could find me something for a morning snack?**

I'm a little surprised you want a morning snack. You haven't been eating particularly well in the mornings. Actually, I was just about to go shopping online. Should we look for a good morning snack?

**What are you looking for online? Something for me?**

A dog bed for Brito. He keeps trying to sleep in a storage container in my closet. I think he wants a bed that is more enclosed like a nest.

**That sounds like something he would enjoy. So what are you buying for me?**

Honestly, I didn't think you needed anything, but now I'm getting a little queasy at the thought of walking away from this computer without something in the shopping cart for you.

**Need? Are you serious? What has need got to do with it? My days on this earth are numbered, you know.**

Everyone's days on this earth are numbered.

**Well, mine are more numbered than yours. So numbered, in fact, that you should buy me something.**

Like what?

**A new dog bed!**

You already have one in every room of the house.

**Hmm. How about some special treats? We could do the automatic renewal thing - you know, where they just keep sending more whether you remember or not? Maybe if we bought a sizable backup supply we wouldn't have any more bedtime debacles! Oh, look here! They have duck and cherry treats! Now what are the odds of that?**

That is amazing. So you're not going to be happy with the packing paper from Brito's new dog bed and my homemade morsels?

**Nope. I'll take the duck and cherry treats, please. Are you getting the express delivery? My days are numbered you know.**

Yeah, you already told me. But no, we are not getting the express delivery service.

**I will endeavor to stay alive until the delivery arrives.**

How thoughtful of you. And Raika? When those treats arrive, I hope you eat them!

**Why wouldn't I? I've always had a soft spot for duck and cherry. Now I have something to look forward to!**

Just remember that when they show up. Lately it seems that some days your eyes are bigger than your stomach.

# Part Two

# Chapter 22:
## The Raika-Mobile

## Raika & Mom

**Mom, I have concerns.**

About what?

**My sleep last night. It was not restful.**

In the RV? We're practicing! So everyone gets settled in before the real deal.

**What kind of practice do we need?**

Well, for starters, I learned how to flush the toilet.

**Gotta start somewhere, I guess.**

Important, in my book. Plus I turned on the heater and boiled water.

**Yes, but enough about you. Now can we talk about me?**

Of course. What's on your mind?

**It's very small. I was not very happy with my sleeping space.**

You got to pick first. You picked the couch. That looked comfy enough?

**Yes, it's fine, but in the middle of the night, I was ready for a change and then Lyra was in the space I wanted. That little area under the bed? I wanted to try that one out.**

You can try all the places, but you can't kick her out if she is already there.

**I know! I stared at her but nothing happened! That used to work perfectly but lately... well, I don't know about**

**Lyra. And there were no other sleeping spaces. So I ran out of "all the places" before I even started trying them out.**

Unfortunately, there are not a lot of choices in an RV.

**So anyway, then I tried to sleep for a bit, but I got thirsty and there was no water!**

Oh, good point. We need a water dish. I'll add that to the list.

**Plus everyone kept getting up and moving around. It was not restful at all.**

That's why we're practicing. So when we actually get to real camping, we'll have a nice routine down.

**Well, it all seemed a little silly when I could see our house from the window.**

Just be patient. We'll go somewhere this afternoon for a quick outing and you'll love it! Not sure I mentioned this, but one of the reasons we bought it was just for you. Now we can take you places and you won't be cramped. I know you need to get up and stretch out more than you used to, and you do like to go on mini-adventures, so I was thinking this might make it easier.

**Very thoughtful, Mom, but the backyard is not an adventure.**

As I said, we're just practicing! But no worries, adventures will follow as soon we have our feet under us.

**I'm going to give you the benefit of the doubt on this occasion, but just know that I have concerns, and this might end up being a particularly ripe opportunity for a string of "I told you so's" in our near future.**

## Later that afternoon...

**It's a beach-mobile!**

I told you that you'd like it.

**You didn't say it was a beach-mobile!**

Well, it's not, really. It's an RV. It can take us lots of places, but if you want to call it your beach-mobile, that's fine with me. We decided to start with the beach because it's pretty close to us. Did you have a good day?

**Did I have a good day?! Didn't you see me running around? Kicking up my heels?! I had a great day! I didn't even mind sharing my great day with Lyra and Brito!**

I think we all had a pretty good time. Even if you did ruin my cool pictures.

**What? I didn't ruin your pictures.**

Yes, you did. In every picture, I got the other dogs sitting nicely looking at the camera. And there you are, wandering around. Every. Single. Picture. I'm surprised no one asked why I trained the other dogs but not you.

**Well, some of the time I didn't think you gave me the best space. You know, front and center?**

So next time you want to be in the middle?

**That might work. And don't press the button until my ears are up and I'm looking good.**

I think it would be very nice to have a picture of all three Fenzi dogs, sitting nicely, looking at the camera. With an interesting background, like that Doggy Buddha sculpture we saw.

**Nah. Not interested in a family portrait. But that beach-**

**mobile! That is a fine thing. Thank you for getting me that.**

You're welcome. But... it's not a beach-mobile. Why don't we call it the Raika-mobile! That might be a bit more accurate, and then we might feel inspired to take it more places - with you inside.

**Excellent. Just excellent!**

## Chapter 23:
### Raika Refuses to Eat

## Mom & Raika

Raika! Breakfast is warmed and ready. We have beef with stuffing today!

**Hmm. Not so hungry this morning.**

How can you say that? This is perfect for you! You love stuffing!

**Eh. Not looking too appetizing.**

You have to eat it or you'll get a tummy ache with your pills.

**I don't want pills this morning.**

I'm using your peanut butter pill pockets - you like that!

**Nope. Not today.**

Seriously, Raika. You have to eat it. Otherwise, I will have to stuff the pills down your throat with butter. And then you will have to eat something, or you'll get a tummy ache for sure.

**Nope.**

I'm going to give your breakfast to the other dogs.

**Okay.**

Oooh, Lyra, beef! And Brito, here's a piece of stuffing celery for you.

**Go for it, Brito! How often do you have the opportunity to eat celery?**

Raika, stop that! It's not his fault that he's small and can't eat many extras. Here, this one's for you; it looks like a bit of giblet cooked in broth. How can you resist?

**Easily.**

Then Brito gets it. Maybe it will take the sting out of the celery. Lyra, here's more for you! And Brito, you get a tiny piece of Raika's pill pocket... Raika, here's a different piece of stuffing. Do you want that?

**Nope.**

Then Brito gets that, too. Huh. A pecan. Do you like nuts? Raika, here's a pecan for you.

**That's actually pretty good.**

Excellent. Pecans for Raika. Celery for Brito, and beef and stuffing for Lyra.

**Yeah, that really is good. I like the crunch.**

I had no idea you even liked nuts - learn something new every day. Have a few more of those... Brito, here's more off the edge of Raika's pill pocket for you.

**Okay, enough is enough! Stop giving him my pill pocket. I'll eat it.**

Super. I assure you it's excellent. Oh, wait. Here's another pecan. Use that to wash down your pill pocket.

**I've eaten a bit. Happy now?**

Almost!

**What's the problem? I ate the pill pocket and a few nuts.**

That was very little food you ate. Enough for the pill, but not enough for your health. You need to eat more.

**Am I the only one who is overwhelmed by the irony of this conversation?**

I assume you are referring to the diet?

**Or the hunger games, as the potentially more apt descriptor.**

It is true that in our modern age we spend a whole lot of time and energy either trying to gain or lose weight and not much just staying put.

**Dogs don't actually have that problem. Just saying.**

Regardless, you've dropped about a pound under your ideal weight, so go ahead and finish up your breakfast.

**Yeah. I have a bit of a tummy ache, so I'll pass. I can still walk just fine.**

But you didn't eat very much.

**Maybe in a while I'll be hungry, like after a walk. We can try something to eat then.**

But what about now? You should have something to eat.

**But right now I'm not hungry.**

I understand that. But if you ate something, then I would feel better.

**How did this become about you?**

Raika, I worry. You've always been a good eater your whole life, so when you start missing meals, it worries me. That is what moms do: we worry. If you eat a little something, I will worry less.

**Is this going to be one of those days when you start thinking everything I do has a Very Deep Meaning? For example, if I miss a meal, then you think I have stomach cancer, right? Well, how about just assuming it's a little stomach bug - nothing more or less than that?**

For God's sake. Why did you have to bring up stomach cancer?

**It was just an example!**

Look, I have some leftover broth from last night. How about you eat that? Just a little liquid to keep you well hydrated and soak those nuts to make them easier to digest.

**I'd rather go for a walk.  Can I have an early walk?**

Sure! We'll go for a walk as soon as you drink your broth. I've warmed it up and everything.

**Fine.  Are you going to stand there watching me drink?**

I'm keeping you company.

**Even licking the edges - see?  So everything is fine.  Go ahead and look it up on your trusty computer; signs of stomach cancer are eliminated when the patient drinks her broth.  No stomach cancer, okay?**

There you go again.

# Chapter 24:
## Brito the Sheep

## Mom & Raika

Raika... Raika? Raika, where are you?

**Here.**

Where is here?

**In the hallway.**

What are you doing in the hallway?

**Nothing.**

Where is Brito?

**He's here with me.**

You and Brito are in the hallway together, doing nothing? Raika, what are you doing?

**I'm using my imagination.**

Using your imagination? What are you imagining?

**Well, if I use my imagination, I see Brito as a little sheep! He's white, sort of wiry, and little. Plus he's kind of nervous.**

Brito is not usually nervous. What are you doing to Brito?

**I'm practicing being a sheepdog. I have him pinned in the corner. Do you want to see what happens if I take a step toward him? I can make him squeak!**

Raika, let him out!

**Whoa! Nothing to get excited about. Relax! I've set him**

free. See? He's just fine. All I was doing was staring at him, you know, fulfilling my heritage! Being a sheepdog!

No more of that, do you hear me?

Okay. Let's go for a swim, then. I wouldn't have even started in on my sheepdog nature if I weren't bored.

It's too cold to swim now that summer is over.

Fine - then let's see about a walk!

I don't want to walk with you right now. I'm irritated.

Mom, I'm a dog. There's no point in holding a grudge. See, look! Brito is fine! He's moved on. You should, too. Grab a warm jacket and let's hit the trail. Did you notice the leaves on the trail last time we were out there? They smell delicious, all mixed in with the damp soil. Autumn really is a fantastic time of year!

I think you get more out of smelling the rotting leaves than I do, but I do love when the air is crisp and clean from the rains.

Grab your jacket and let's go. This day is shaping up to be a fine one after all!

## Raika & Mom

Mom, I have a story for you! Are you ready?

I am!

You are getting sleepy... look deep into my eyes... your eyelids are drooping...

They are?

Shhh. Your tongue is getting heavy...

My tongue is getting heavy? Raika, what are you doing?

**Nothing.**

Nothing? Last time you said "nothing," you had poor little Brito trapped in a corner squeaking while you pretended he was a sheep.

**You have a memory like an elephant.**

So, did you have a story for me or not?

**Not exactly.**

No story? But you promised me one.

**That was only a partial truth. Or maybe not a truth at all.**

What is the truth? The full truth?

**I was trying to hypnotize you.**

Why on earth would you want to do that?

**I was just thinking I could get a few extras.**

Extras?

**Yeah. Extras. Extra walks. Extra swims. Extras!**

I see. The deprivation around here is getting to you, huh? I assume you also want extra food?

**Well, it's more a matter of autonomy. Right now, everything is about you and your habitual ways of thinking. I would like to make some decisions, too. And frankly, my appetite has been a little unpredictable lately, so I'm thinking more about things we do together.**

That's hard, Raika, because it's kind of non-stop with you. You always want something. If I accommodated you every time, I think you would become a full-time job. Besides, I'm not sure you'd make good decisions. Remember Brito the Sheep?

**Now you're harping.**

Well, I'm the one that has to work to pay the bills. Generally, that means that you have to work around my schedule.

**Possibly there is room for compromise.**

This conversation is making me nervous; I feel like Brito stuck in the corner.

**How about this? You can make all of the decisions when you are already doing something and I have a request. For example, when you go into the bathroom, I will not expect you to drop everything to accommodate me. Of course, I will continue to escort you for reasons of safety. When you are eating a meal, I will not expect you to stop eating to take me swimming. However, it would not be unreasonable for you to flip a few stray morsels my way since that is a matter of sharing, and sharing is a good human habit, especially now that I have dropped an extra pound and am technically underweight. And when you are working to earn that dog food money, I will be understanding about that as well. But when you are playing on Facebook or just sitting around or working extra hours for no particular reason at all? Then I think you should consider what I might want to do.**

Honestly Raika, I thought I already did that.

**You get stuck in conventional thinking. For example, when you have free time and you could take me for a walk, rather than looking at my hopeful face and accommodating me, you ask yourself if we've already taken a walk. But where is it written in the Great Book of Rules that we can only take one walk per day? And when we head out, we almost always go in one direction with no turning back for another round of investigation or a second sniff. Stretch your imagination a little, and let go of some of those conventions!**

My scalp is prickling. I wonder if that's how Brito felt stuck in the corner like a sheep.

**You really are stuck on that incident! That was last week, and you've managed to bring it up four times in a single conversation! Another human foible that is seriously unattractive.**

You're right. I'll work harder to let it go.

**You know, today - with the sun shining and glinting off the surface of that shiny blue pool water - today would be a fantastic day to start a new habit! Do you see me standing here, with my hopeful face turned towards the pool?**

Indeed I do, Raika. Indeed I do. Now consider this: it's cold out there! That water looks lovely - and cold! Have you, by chance, looked at the thermometer on the wall?

**There you go again! Being practical. And here I am, trying to wring the life out of my last few weeks or months on this earth.**

Weeks or months? Look at you! You're doing amazingly well! I think you need to chat with Lyra more and see about absorbing some of her optimistic spirit.

**Rather than observing the Great Book of Rules, maybe consulting the actuarial tables for dogs would be better suited to your delusional nature.**

Raika, seriously. You're doing great. Summer will roll around soon enough and you'll be back to paddling all over the place.

**Well, since my attempts at hypnotism have not led to the attention I'm seeking, I'm going to try something new. Hold on a second. Okay - now. Is it working?**

Is what working?

**I'm telepathing you.**

You're what?

**Telepathing you!**

Never heard of that.

**I'm talking to you through your head! I've tried the direct route: tapping your leg, puffing, and looking sad. You totally ignored me. And my attempts at hypnotism were met with confusion or possibly outright scorn. Which would have been fine except it didn't work. So now I'm telepathing you.**

Oh. I thought you were going back to resting.

**Nope. So how's it going?**

What?

**My telepathing. Are we going for a walk?**

Right now?

**Try me! Say, "Raika, do you want to go for a walk?" and see how fast I head for the door!**

Hate to break it to you, but you're almost deaf as a doorknob, so as long as you're staring at the pool, it's not going to work. I would have to pat you to get your attention.

**Yeah, okay. That's fine, too. Or you could try telepathing me back. But for sure, a pat should break me right out of my concentrative state.**

Concentrative state?

**Don't worry about it. Let's just go.**

# Chapter 25:
## Snowbirds

### Raika & Mom

**Rain again. I think it's time that we became snowbirds, especially with winter right around the corner.**

Snowbirds? Raika, we're in California. It doesn't snow here.

**It's just an expression. I mean that we should go somewhere even warmer than California in the winter. Somewhere that I could swim year-round! If you want, we could call ourselves "rain birds." We leave to escape the rain.**

Ah. I see where this is going. So you think we should fly off to Florida or some other warm place so you can swim now that we've come to the end of the season?

**Yes, exactly.**

And what should we do about the other dogs?

**They could stay here with Dad.**

Dad doesn't get to come along?

**Well, Dad would definitely be welcome, but then there would be a problem about who would take care of the other dogs.**

I would think the entire family would have to come. And since you're the only one who's obsessive about swimming year-round, that seems kind of extreme.

**Extreme? I'm old! How much more time do you think I have to enjoy life, which means swimming! That right there should be enough to convince you to give me what I want. And what I want is to be a snowbird! Or, in my**

**case, a snowdog. If you don't like Florida, how about Australia? We could go to Australia. My friends in Australia love me!**

That they do, but Australia has a long quarantine. I don't think you want to sit in a kennel for months, do you?

**Do they have a pool at the kennel? Could I spend my days by the pool?**

I'm pretty sure they don't have a pool. Nor will you be able to go for long walks, and I'm not convinced you'll have a comfy dog bed.

**Some hardcore deprivation right there in Australia. All right, then it's settled. Florida, here we come!**

Don't hold your breath.

**I'm awesome at that, but maybe that's not what you meant. So, since I think you may be resisting me, have you considered a pool heater or a rain cover?**

Raika, listen. It's not that cold here, so we don't need a pool heater. And we don't need a cover, because it doesn't rain that much.

**Then why can't I swim now?**

I'm a little afraid to open up this conversation again because I know what you'll say.

**What will I say?**

That if I really loved you, then I could put on more clothes to keep warm and add a rain jacket so that you could swim all year long. Because you're not going to be here forever, being an old dog and all.

**Yeah. I could see me saying something like that. So how about it?**

Let's go for a walk, and talk about this later.

**More likely, we'll resume this conversation never.**

## Chapter 26:
## Leashes Should be Illegal

### Raika & Mom

**Leashes should be illegal.**

Leashes keep you safe when you're not making good decisions.

**If I've heard you say it once, I've heard you say it a hundred times. Leashes teach humans to ignore their dogs.**

The difference is that most people's dogs aren't deaf. When they are, a leash is a pretty good idea.

**I am not deaf.**

Fine. Leashes are a good idea for dogs who have gone rogue.

**I am neither deaf nor rogue! Okay, maybe I am deaf - but rogue? Besides, I prefer to think of myself as realistic; rogue has such a negative connotation.**

Realism has nothing to do with this conversation, Raika! You didn't need that leftover fast food that I saw you eyeing on the side of the trail. Far from it. What you need is your nutritious breakfasts - the ones you've taken to skipping a little too often. Can you explain how it is possible that you miss meals regularly, and yet you never miss an opportunity to scavenge something nasty and rotten?

**I'm weak with hunger as a result of missing breakfast.**

I was actually thinking the opposite; you pulled awfully hard toward that bag on the ground. I was impressed. I didn't know you could pull that hard anymore.

**I can feel my muscles being consumed for energy. The heart will go next. That's what happens to starving animals.**

Exaggerate much?

**At my age, I doubt this muscle wasting can be stopped.**

I'm not sure that eating day old fast food is going to do much
for your muscle tone, and while you have indeed lost a couple of
pounds, I'm not sure I'd put you in the category of starving to death.

**I never cease to be amazed by how little faith you have
in my understanding of my own body. Anyway, we were
discussing leashes. I don't see anyone putting a leash on
you, and we all know how you are about going toward
shiny objects. No one will even go shopping with you!**

The difference is that I like to LOOK at shiny objects. I do not grab
them. And when did this conversation become about me?

**Whatever. I'm going to suggest that Dad buy you a leash
for Christmas. After a few weeks of wearing a leash, you
can let me know what you think.**

## Chapter 27:
## Kidnapped!

Raika & Mom

**I see that your suitcases are in the front hall again. You're going somewhere - just when I thought you were settling in here at home!**

I'm flying to Texas this weekend, but I'll only be gone for four days. I'll be back before you even notice that I'm missing.

**Well, in the interests of not being passive-aggressive, shall I tell you how I feel about this? Just outright? Because I will definitely notice that you're missing.**

Of course, Raika. I always want to hear how you feel.

**All right, then. You'll walk out the front door and drive away with Dad. At first, I will be sad and forlorn. I will watch the car rolling down the hill from the window. Then I will lie down in the entryway, put my head on my paws, and wait. That's when I'm a real bundle of unhappiness. Next, I enter the hopeful phase. I will hope that you'll change your mind and come back through the door, not that it has ever happened. Then Dad will come home without you, hours will go by, and still you won't return. Dad will give me dinner. Right about then, I'll know that you have not changed your mind. So I'll eat my dinner, go find Dad, and sit with him.**

**All of this sadness and hopefulness takes place prior to the panic phase. As you know, I don't sleep much during the day, so when you are gone, I spend the entire time thinking about you and wishing you would come back. But it's at night that I get panicky. I'll go to your side of the bed, but you won't be there. I'll return to Dad's side, frequently checking to see whether you might have come back after**

**all. Of course, you haven't. The next morning I will try to dredge up a smidgen of hope, but it's too late for that. All I will feel is hopelessness.**

**That is when I'll enter my lonely phase. I will look out the window one last time, but you won't be there. Then I'll attach myself to Dad and follow him around for the rest of the day since I figure that if anything terrible happens to you, he'll be the first to know. And then for the following days, I will alternate between hope, sadness, panic, loneliness, and anger over being left again. To their credit, Brito and Lyra will try to make me feel better, but it won't help very much.**

**Then, as suddenly as you left, you will reappear through the front door! I will be overjoyed, unable to believe my good fortune. You have returned! But then you leave again. So, there it is in a nutshell: how I feel when you are gone. I hope that wasn't too passive-aggressive?**

I don't know what to say. I feel terrible.

**I'll admit that gives me a certain amount of pleasure. Misery loves company.**

I promise you, Raika, I will be traveling less in the future. Within a couple of months, I should be home most of the time. I have been making arrangements to end my travel, but I have to finish up these last commitments.

**I could be dead in a few months.**

I would say that comment is verging on passive-aggressive. But really, I'm sorry. I want to be here with you and Lyra and Brito and the human family. Soon, I promise.

**Okay. I'll be waiting for that. And Mom?**

Yeah?

**It's not passive-aggressive. I'm getting older now. I**

**keep trying to point that out - gently - but I hope you're thinking about things.**

We have time.

**We need to start talking about it.**

I'm sure we'll know when it's time to talk about it.

**You're a tough nut to crack, but I'll let it go for now.**

## Lyra & Raika

Raika, what will happen to Mom after you die?

**She'll be fine, Lyra. You and Brito will still be here.**

I don't think so.

**She will.**

That's not what I see. She structures her whole day around you: feeding you, walking you, worrying about you. She's so soft.

**Lyra, soft is not the same as weak. Mom may be soft, but she is also strong. When the last dog in this family died, she went away for a few days. To the beach, I think, but I'm not sure because she didn't take any of us with her. And when she came back, she just resumed living. I'm sure some days were hard, but she came back to us.**

I wonder if that time was different because Mom didn't know that dog was dying. She didn't have all of the special rituals and routines that she has for you.

**When the time comes, Mom will start letting go. Something tells me she might be getting there, a little bit.**

How will she start letting go?

**She'll start thinking about new routines. The new things**

that she'll want to do when the time comes. Maybe on some level she is already thinking about those things: what she will do with all that time that we spend together now.

So she'll just... move on?

No, I don't really think that's possible. Anyway, that's not something a person gets to choose. Just because Mom is soft doesn't mean she's fragile. She's probably one of the strongest people you will ever know.

I don't understand.

She'll feel the loss deeply, but she'll absorb it rather than fight it, so she'll be okay after a while. That's why she's a soft person - she feels everything. A hard person tries to shut out those feelings when sad things happen, but they can't keep it up forever. It's probably better for her to go ahead and feel the loss, and hope that time passes quickly so that she can move on to more positive feelings. Mom will spend her time thinking about all of the wonderful memories we had together, and when it's too much, she'll think about her human family – that they are all very healthy and happy, and she will be grateful for that. She'll look at you and Brito, and be grateful for both of you. She'll be grateful for me, for all that we shared together. She just doesn't talk about it. And at some point, she'll probably think about getting another dog.

What kind of dog?

I don't know. I don't know everything that Mom thinks, but I know she'll find a way through.

What will my job be?

Just be yourself. A pleasant dog. She likes dogs, you know.

And Brito, too? Just be a dog?

**More or less. But it would be good if he could learn to shut his mouth. I don't know how she can think with all the racket he makes; I sure can't.**

I hope you're right. What do you think Mom will do with herself? Maybe she'll go back to working, staring at her phone and computer all the time.

**You know? I don't think so.**

Then what will she do?

**She will walk. And she will write.**

## Raika & Mom

To: Mom@fake.emailaddress.com

From: Raika@fake.emailaddress.com

Hi Mom,

I haven't heard from you in more than twenty-four hours. I'm wondering if you're all right? Did another hurricane come? A tornado? I was anxious, so I decided to send you an email; I hope that's okay.

I'm trying to keep up hope, but twenty-four hours is a long time. I keep thinking that you probably only worked for eight hours. That leaves sixteen hours for you to remember to send me a little note. Which leads me to conclude...

You could be dead.

Love, Raika

Hi Raika,

I'm doing fine! Right here in Texas, just like I said I would be.
They're taking very good care of me, feeding me good food, and I
have a nice hotel room, too, but I miss you and I miss being home.
I'd rather sleep in my own bed, eating my own food, and seeing you
curled up on your bed next to mine. I hope you're going for walks,
and eating your meals, and getting along with the other dogs.

Love, Mom


**Hi Mom,**

**So glad to hear from you! I'm a little concerned that
you're so chipper considering  you went away to work. Is
it possible that you are being forced to write these things
by your captors? Of course, if you were, they would read
this first and you would not be free to tell me the truth! I
think the next time you travel, we need to have some code
words to ensure that I can send help should it come to pass
that you are in a life-threatening situation and are not able
to speak freely. So anyway, I hope you really are where
you say you are - working - and that you will, indeed,
come home again.**

**Love, Raika**


Hi Raika,

I have not been kidnapped! I'll be starting my flight home tomorrow.
I've heard that we may run into severe weather, so the flight could
be cancelled, or maybe we'll just have a really rough flight. I hope
not, but wish me luck on the way home! If the flight is cancelled, I'll
send you a note so you won't worry.

Love, Mom

**Hi Mom,**

**I understand - you're not free to speak. I'll be thinking about you every minute while you plan your escape. Best of luck, and I want you to know that I love you so much no matter what happens!**

**Love, Raika**

## Raika & Mom

**I'm glad you're home, Mom! But I'm also alternating between mad and happy. Happy that you're alive! And mad that you didn't think about how I might feel at home worrying about you. I've been worried sick! You could've responded to my email and at least told me that you had escaped and were attempting to make your way home.**

I definitely was not trying to upset you, Raika, but I didn't realize that you expected an email after I told you I was heading home. And Raika? There were no captors. I was at work in Texas - just like I said I would be.

**Remember when you gave Chris a phone? The expectation was that he would text you and tell you where he was. I remember that you were pretty upset when he didn't do that. You were mad at him for not telling you where he was, and happy that he was alive when you found him. So you should know exactly how I feel!**

The difference is that Chris and I had made an agreement beforehand. He knew that he was supposed to text me or come home on time, and he didn't. I came home to you on time!

**Then we need to set our expectations for future trips. Next time you travel, a quick email will do just fine.**

You know I'm not traveling for a while, right?  I'm home for the next few weeks.  And when I travel, I mostly work.  There's not much to chat about.

**Well then, you can tell me what you're eating!  That's always a good topic of conversation.**

I could certainly do that.  This weekend I had a muffaletta sandwich for the first time.  It was delicious!

**See?  We have our first topic of conversation all picked out!  Now let's go for a walk.  By the time we get home, I will have forgiven you about 90%.  I'll reserve the final 10% until I see what's for dinner.**

## Chapter 28: The Walking List

### Raika & Mom

**Good for you for getting outdoors for our walk in the rain! I'm proud of you! Even if your optimistic spirit did kind of bite you in the butt when you left your raincoat behind, thinking it was only going to be a light shower.**

What's that got to do with being an optimist?

**Well, a pessimist like me knows that if something good happens, it's simply a reminder that something bad is just around the corner. Today is an excellent example. If the sun shows up in the middle of a rainy day, it simply predicts more bad weather. An optimist like you thinks it actually means a change of weather. In this case, we can clearly see that it doesn't pay to be an optimist. That is why you are sopping wet from head to toe. Regardless, I have an idea to ensure that this won't happen again. We need to create a "Going for a Walk" checklist. That way, when it's time to leave the house, you can make sure we haven't forgotten anything. Not that I'm harping, but there was that day that we left without any snacks, and we don't want that to happen again. I still have nightmares over that, you know.**

Raika, that was months ago.

**Feels like yesterday. Anyway, first you need a leash, poop bags, and snacks for me.**

Got it.

**Be sure to put a rain jacket and rain boots for you on the list. And while I'm thinking about it, go back up and**

underline **"snacks for Raika."** **It would be a tragedy if those were forgotten, and since we have some history there, let's just nip that possibility in the bud.**

Okay, I have those things, and "snacks" is underlined. Anything else?

**How about a camera? That way you can take pictures of me looking beautiful. Today I think it would've been worthwhile to take a picture of yourself - a selfie! You were looking kind of pitiful, all chilled and soggy. I think it would have been kind of funny to post that, maybe on Instagram?**

You could be a little more charitable considering that I was out there because of you. And frankly, I'm a bit surprised that you are suggesting pictures since that would mean bringing my phone out of my pocket. I thought you wanted my phone to stay in my pocket?

**Charitable?! I started this conversation by telling you that I was proud of you! Now if you would only adopt a little more of my suspicious nature, you wouldn't run into these problems. Anyway, now that we have our list, future walks should be more organized with less left to chance. We should be able to get through this season with no worries at all. As far as your phone, you've made some good progress there! You should be proud of yourself! I'm thinking it might be time to give you a little freedom and see if you are responsible enough to bring it out on occasion - use it for the briefest and most momentous events, and then put it back again. Do you think you can do that?**

Honestly, I'm not sure. It might be easier to keep it tucked away than to try and bring it out and then put it back again. But I'm willing to try - to document our most "momentous events," as you call them.

**I think you can do it; give it a shot and we'll see how it goes.**

## Chapter 29:
### The Best Gift of All

Raika & Mom

**Did you hear all the nice things the vet said about me?**

Yes, I did; I was there the entire time!

**The part about how good I look? How well I move? About my balance and all of that?**

Yep. I heard those parts too.

**She raved about how cooperative I was.**

She did!

**And did you hear how she said that I was well-behaved?**

Indeed. And I was very careful not to ask you to do anything, lest we ruin her good impression.

**That was good thinking.**

I thought so.

**But there was no cookie jar in the exam room.**

Ah, now that you mention it... no, I didn't notice one.

**I was looking on the way out and didn't see one anywhere. And you know those big frog-shaped wading pools that can be filled with stuffed toys for the good dogs?**

Yeah.

**They didn't have one of those either.**

Hmm. No, there wasn't much there of interest to a dog.

**No.**

No.

**So.**

So what, Raika?

**Possibly a small stuffed toy would be in order for a well-behaved dog with a limited number of days left. To ensure future cooperation?**

Ah. Yes. I believe we have some of those. I bought them for Brito.

**A toy for the dog so highly thought of by the vet! Especially those little Brito toys, as I've observed that you now lock them in his pen.**

Yeah, they kept ending up on your dog bed, so now I lock them in. And now that I think about it, how about a snack for you, as well? I have no problem giving you two rewards for your excellent behavior. Plus, the vet did mention that you'd lost a bit more weight.

**I appreciate the sentiment, but I'm not feeling too hungry right now. Since you brought up the topic, we need to start talking about a few things. My weight, for example. I'm losing weight.**

Let me see what we have in the way of hot dogs; even if you're not at your most hungry, maybe you will enjoy that.

**When are we going to talk? I see your suitcases in the hallway. Are you traveling again?**

Yeah, I meant to say something to you about that. I'm heading to England for a week. As far as your weight - the vet didn't seem too concerned, so we're just keeping an eye on it right now. It's only a few pounds.

**I hate that you travel. It used to make me a little sad, but now I really need you here with me. Dad and the kids**

**need you, too! There's too much to get done, and it makes it really hard for everyone when you're not here. And while it is true I'm thinking mostly about me, the truth is that the whole family wants you to stay home more.**

Raika, I know. I cannot tell you how much I'd rather be home with you right now. I promise, just one week! I'll be thinking about you and the family constantly.

**We don't want your thoughts - we want you.**

## Raika & Mom

**To: Mom@fake.emailaddress.com**

**From: Raika@fake.emailaddress.com**

**Hi Mom,**

**I was looking at your Facebook page this morning. Wherever you are, I see that you have a big, fluffy bed to sleep in. Looks comfy. Looks like you also have tea and biscuits for a bedtime snack. Are the biscuits tasty? They seem to be plentiful. Plentiful food is good.**

**And a big bath, too? Like a swimming pool with warm water, just for the winter months. Must be nice.**

**And even warm jammies. You seem very happy there without me.**

**Anyway, I just wanted to remind you that I am here at home, waiting for you.**

**No need to respond. I'm fine. I'm taking a nap here on the hard floor next to your bed. Waiting for you. Dinner was the usual. It was okay; I ate a few bites. I've run out of the treats that I like, so there will be no bedtime snack for me, and Dad didn't seem to understand that he needed to make more.**

**Anyway. Bye.**

Hi Raika,

I'm so glad you told me about the bedtime snacks being low. I forgot to tell Dad, but don't worry, he knows now, and that will be fixed.

The days are very long on this trip. I'm either traveling from one location to the other, or working all morning and afternoon and then going out with groups of people in the evening, or finishing up my routine work that follows me even when I travel. There's not much time to write emails. Everyone is very friendly, and they are even asking about you! I tell them that you're getting older but are doing super well at your age, and I thank them for asking. I've also met some fantastic dogs here, but it's not the same as being home with you.

Just a couple more days and I'll be back. Take care of everyone while I'm gone, and keep a close eye on the kids - Dad can use your help when I'm not there.

Love, Mom

**Hi Mom,**

**Guess what? Dad wanted me to eat breakfast, so he added warm tripe to my food. I ate every bite! Better yet, the house retained that delicate smell for most of the morning! It was pure genius, and I think that tripe should be a regular part of my future if you come back. Also, I got some chalupa for dinner! "Ask and ye shall receive," is my motto. And if that doesn't work, then stop eating and see if that gets the ball rolling; I tried a twenty-four hour stint without food and that certainly got everyone's attention. So while I am still glad that you are coming home, it's okay here.**

**I am looking forward to seeing you and all of our gifts soon. I hope you were able to fit them into the suitcase.**

**Love, Raika**

## Raika & Mom

**Mom! Once again you have escaped the claws of tragedy. Or is it the jaws of tragedy? I get confused about some of those over the top expressions these days. Regardless, I'm so glad you're back!**

I'm glad to be back! Are you doing okay?

**About as well as can be expected for a confused and arthritic dog in the last days of her life. What's in your suitcase?**

All sorts of things. Clothes, gifts, other stuff.

**I'll help you unpack, just in case there are gifts for me.**

I have no doubt that there are gifts for you.

**Oooh! Look! These are clearly for me! And you got things, too! We'll make a pile for you on one side of the bed, and one for me on the other. My pile is growing! I see duck and plum treats - what a great twist on an old favorite! And duck and oats! Kangaroo? That's a new one. Do they have kangaroos in England? And fish treats - I'll give those to Lyra. She thinks she likes fish, and it's always good to appear generous. Or maybe Brito. He eats everything. What a great big pile for me!**

You made out pretty well. I got fudge, chocolate, a hat, biscuits, and some training equipment. And – oh yes – have a look at this: for Brito, a little bear toy!

**I wonder if Brito might want me to have that little bear toy?**

Your pile looks pretty good already.

**True. Not a bad haul.**

Yes, Raika, it was a pretty good haul. Not all presenters get gifts, you know, and even fewer get things to take back to their dogs.

**It's because my days are numbered. It's not as clear why you got so many gifts, but I'm not going to worry about it. My pile is quite large and that certainly counts for something.**

Raika? I have another gift for you.

**Seriously? Where is it?**

It's not a thing. It's a change in our lifestyle. I'm not going to travel anymore for work. I'm going to stay home now.

**Really?**

Really. It's time to be here with you and the family.

**Because I'm dying?**

I want to be here because we both know that your time will come - it is inevitable. Whenever you miss a meal, I start to panic, and then I stop and look a little more carefully at you. I know that you've been trying to talk to me - your little jokes about the end of life - and I've been avoiding that. I don't want to joke about that. We have time, I'm sure of it, but I know that your death will come and I'm trying to make sense of it. For sure I want to spend as much time with you as possible. That is why I have decided to stop traveling. I don't want to worry about you when I'm not here, spending my time wishing I could be home with you. I need to be here. Plus, Dad and the kids need me, too. I need to focus harder on life outside of work. I miss the whole family.

**This is great, Mom! I'm so excited! Soon though... maybe we need to start having some serious conversations? It's okay if it's not quite yet - I'm just happy that you're going to be home now!**

And I'm happy that you're happy!

**What a day! I got a huge pile of gifts, and now you're staying home - the very best gift of all!**

So Raika, to answer your question? Yes. Soon we can start having those conversations that seem to be very important to you. I don't know how I'll manage when you're not here, and I'm not exactly sure what you want to talk about, but I'm ready to try - not today, but very soon. So when you want to talk, I'm going to do my best to listen and hear what you have to say.

**Soon, Mom. Soon we'll start to talk. There are things we need to discuss, and we can't wait too much longer or it could be too late.**

## Mom

I was wrong about death: death waits for no one. Of course I know that, but knowing and feeling are not the same. There is no contradiction between knowing and refusing to believe what you know. Or, as Raika would say, there is no end to the number of ways humans manage self-deceit. Indeed, it appears to be the human condition, and this round I am first in line.

It seems a cruel deception to have a dog with very few external signs of aging to remind me that I need to prepare. Where is the frosty white muzzle? The stiff gait? Where is the old dog?

So how might I prepare? Does one practice thinking or behaving differently? Spend time doing things alone to get used to it? Look for joy in solitude? Surely there are various silver linings?

I agreed to this. I chose Raika knowing that her lifespan would be mismatched to mine.

Where I erred - and it was a significant error - was my lack of recognition that not all dogs will create exactly the same impact as others. I miscalculated the capacity of some dogs to wind themselves around one's heart in inexplicable ways. How might I remove the tentacles that are embedded without ripping apart the heart underneath at the same time?

Maybe I am getting ready right now. Maybe I am practicing the experience of worry and grief so that when the real deal arrives, when she passes, I will have either deadened my heart or used it all up - to the same effect. With my travel schedule wrapped up, I can stay home with her right in front of me, demanding more than her fair share of my time and attention. So here I am: drowning by choice, home with an aging dog and a family who haven't seen enough of me for too long, consumed by work at the expense of life. I want to fix it but I don't know how.

Of course, there is a completely different way to look at it. Look at Raika! So cute-old! I can live with her and admire who she is and all that she brings to me and my life. Why focus on the calendar when she - Raika - still moves with grace and determination? Why focus on death and worry when she is still here? Without any real evidence of decline, what is the harm of holding off altogether? Why worry about a family that grows and talks and laughs and functions, whether I am here or not?

But she wants to talk, and I have promised to listen. What does she want to talk about? She's going to die - of course she is - and my heart will be broken. What else is there to say?

Her time will come. And I need to take a vacation and reconnect with my family.

# Winter 2018/2019

### Chapter 30:
### Raika's Ninja Moves

## Mom & Raika

I have something for you for your half birthday!

**Is it already that time? Wow. Time goes by fast when the end is near.**

Raika, give it a rest. I bought you gifts to celebrate, not to be depressed. Fourteen-and-a-half already!

**Ooh, I see it – that fluffy new bed with pillows for my head? I love it!**

I know! I thought you might really like that part. Plus, do you see how I put a blanket on top of it? That's so you can make your bed fluffy. You like making a fluffy bed.

**I love having a fluffy bed!**

And look! There's even more for you! Check out the wastepaper basket; there are fresh boxes and papers to shred.

**Ooh, that's the good kind of shredding paper. Oh, and chewing bones! I get all of this, too?**

You do. I bought the bones because it said they smell like bacon and other food, but to be honest, I don't smell it. Maybe you do?

**Well, no. I don't smell it either. But that's okay, we can let Brito and Lyra chew on those. I really do love my gifts! Now just keep Lyra off my bed. If you see her on my bed,**

**I want you to get her off.**

How about she can use it when you're doing other things? But if you come over, I'll get it back for you, okay?

**Okay. But don't forget.**

Raika, can I ask you a question about our walk yesterday morning?

**Sure, what's on your mind?**

Did you know I was a bit nervous about the man on our trail?

**No, you were too far away for me to know that. Those woods have some amazing exploring opportunities packed in there. I was pretty wrapped up in scraping up the frost and sniffing the first-class smells buried just below the surface.**

You didn't? But you came back to my side.

**When I looked over, I thought he was behaving a little oddly. And since you don't have much in the way of teeth, I figured I needed to be there. You can never be too careful, especially since you tend to be ridiculously optimistic. Happy all the time! It's not healthy, you know. It's about time you paid a little attention.**

So all was well, and for sure, nothing happened. And today for your half birthday walk? I thought you stayed closer. I noticed the difference.

**There were more people around - it's a weekend.**

That's true!

**I do pay attention, you know. How do you miss so much? It's my job to keep an eye on the big picture.**

I thought you stayed closer today and I guess I was right.

**I did... And Mom? Lyra is more dog than you think.**

**She's going to do just fine when she's in charge of looking after you.**

What's Lyra got to do with this conversation?

**You'll see. You'll start training her properly and everything will change. That's because she's a dog – and a good one at that.**

I'm talking about going for a walk with a scary man on the trail, and you're talking about Lyra?

**Right now I take care of you, but it's in her. I promise you, from the grave, I'll be saying, "I told you so!"**

The grave? You're doing great, Raika. Only a few minor signs of age. We have plenty of time before we need to worry about that.

**Okey dokey.**

So what about Brito?

**Don't hold your breath on that one.**

## Mom & Raika

See those cookies on the table?

**I do.**

I know you do. That's what I want to talk about.

**What would you like to say?**

Those are my holiday cookies. They belong to me. Don't mess with them.

**I can't; they're pushed too far back. You'd need to move them about nine inches further forward before there's even a reason to have this conversation. Of course, if you pulled out a chair...**

Raika, don't even think about them, or how you might get to them. Nothing. Nada. Not Raika's cookies.

**Okay.**

Stop looking at them.

**Why?**

Because you're intimidating me. I keep wanting to push them just a bit further back.

**Why is it that one day you're practically forcing me to eat, and the next day you don't want me to touch anything?**

There is healthy dinner food, and then there is dessert food. Those cookies? Those are dessert food, specifically for people. They are not for you. When food shows up in your bowl, that is dinner food. For you. When you don't eat the food in your bowl, I worry. Don't make me worry! Plus, I don't understand how one day you're scarfing up everything in sight, and then the next nothing seems to appeal to you. Eat your dinner and I'll be happy.

**Seems like a lot of rules right there. Personally, I prefer to go with the flow. However, I have an idea that might work right now.**

What's that?

**How about if you place a cookie in my bowl? Then it would be dinner food.**

No go. These have a lot of chocolate in them, and that's not for you.

**Worth a try. But if I figure out a way to get on that table, I will feel no compunction about eating some cookies - maybe even a lot of them - since you're not sharing. Or if my appetite suddenly wanes for the effort of finding a way up there, I could simply lick each of them. That would give me a bit of the flavor to remind me of how delicious they could have been if I were actually hungry. A taste of**

**my youth, if you will.**

In your youth, it would not have crossed your mind to take food off the counter. Your loss of manners seems to have come in a reasonably linear fashion with your age. And as a result of that comment, I'm moving them to the back of the counter.

**Damn. Who said honesty was the best policy? Sure didn't do me any favors. I should have just used one of my stealth ninja moves and been done with it.**

Which ninja move are we discussing?

**The one that landed me a cookie off the coffee table last night. Let me tell you how I did it. First, I picked my angle of attack. Next, quiet as a cat, I slipped right up to the edge of the table and snagged it off the plate! It happened so fast you didn't even move!**

I think there's something I need to tell you.

**What's that?**

I knew you were going to steal that cookie. I figured you wanted it more than I did. And one small leftover butter cookie isn't going to kill you.

**Wait a second. You're saying it wasn't my cunning that scored me the cookie?**

Well, I'm sure it contributed. I'm just saying that on this particular occasion, I saw it coming.

**I feel the air going out of my balloon.**

And now I feel bad. Next time I will go to great lengths to block you from the cookie, okay?

**Okay! And then you can watch my ninja moves shine!**

Exactly. May the best player win.

# Part Two

# Chapter 31:
## Pancake Sprinkles and the Business of Sneaking up on People

### Raika & Mom

**Who would've thought that a serving of beef could be enhanced so much by a sprinkling of pancake on top?**

I don't know, Raika. You're not like most dogs.

**It was delicious! Now I'm wondering if pancake sprinkles could enhance other foods. We should look into that. Oh - and maple syrup! I'll bet breakfast could be even better if we added some syrup!**

It's easy for me to add pancake sprinkles to your food. It's less clear that the syrup is a good idea. We're still working to get your tummy troubles under control, so let me think about that, especially since I doubt you enjoy the baths that follow when you end up with another bout of diarrhea. But do I have to stand there sprinkling the pancakes the entire time that you're eating?

**I eat better when I have your company.**

I've noticed. I was wondering if we could find a way to change that a little? For example, how about if I put your food in the bowl and kept you company for the first minute. Then could I go do something else?

**No. That won't work for me.**

Why not?

**Because my food tastes better when you keep me company.**

Maybe you could eat a little bit faster?

**Are you kidding? That wouldn't be good for my digestion.**

Raika, the problem is that I keep forgetting that I'm supposed to be keeping you company. I walk away, so you walk away, and I don't notice that you never finished your breakfast. Lyra is getting quite chubby cleaning up after you. I feel like I'm going from one dieting dog to the next these days.

**I'm not walking away - she's practically taking the food out from under my nose when you're not watching her! You need to stay with me from start to finish, even if it takes me fifteen minutes. To keep yourself occupied, a reasonable solution might be that you could keep sprinkling pancakes over the top while I eat. You can alternate those pancake sprinkles with drizzles of syrup. That will give you something to do. Although I guess that if you really think the syrup causes diarrhea, I would regretfully agree that we might need to leave that off. The frequent baths aren't really working for me.**

I know. Grooming isn't your thing anymore.

**Pedicures are okay, and brushing with the wooden brush is fine, too, but I'm wondering about that other brush you're using. Maybe we need a new brush. I've heard that the skin of... mature dogs... can get thin. It is possible that my skin has matured and now I need a new brush.**

I've noticed you're not a fan of the metal brush - that's the one that gets out the dead undercoat - but I'm not sure how to get around using it altogether.

**While I can hardly believe I'm about to say this, I wonder if it would be helpful to trim or - taking a deep breath here - shave a little bit, just the parts underneath where no one can see. Maybe on my belly, the insides of my legs, and the long hair under my tail. Or, the insides of my fluffy pants; no one will notice if some of that was taken away.**

I'm glad you brought it up because I've been thinking exactly that. Sometimes when your tummy troubles lead to diarrhea, we could clean you up lickety-split if you didn't have those long hairs there in the back. We'll trim those up nice and tidy today, and I'll do it in a way that no one will even notice. You'll look as lovely as ever.

**Excellent. One more thing.**

What's up?

**This business of creeping up on me has got to stop. You seem to be developing a habit of it. For example, today I was enjoying the lovely scents on the breeze outside, and next thing I know, boom! Tap, tap on my side! I thought I was being attacked! Practically hit the ground and peed! What were you thinking?!**

Seriously, Raika, I didn't mean to scare you. I was talking the whole time I walked up. I needed to get your attention so I could bring you in the house before it got any colder, and you didn't see or hear me... I tapped you as gently as I could.

**If you were talking, then maybe you've got laryngitis, because I heard pretty much nothing. Talk a little louder. My ears may not be true ninja quality anymore, but enough that if you put out some effort I would know you were there.**

Probably what happened is that you were so involved in the smells in the air that you weren't paying attention to your surroundings.

**Yes. Probably that is what happened.**

I have an idea. How about if I clap when I walk up to you? I would think that might break through even when you are most deeply concentrating.

**Let's give that a shot. But the creeping... No more of that or you'll scare me right into my grave! My days may be numbered, but no reason to shave more off early.**

Absolutely! I'll start today, right along with your new "barely take anything off and it won't even show" haircut. Might take me a few days to get down some new habits, but I'm trying, okay?

Part Two

# Chapter 32:
## The Five Sisters

### Raika & Mom

**I don't know how this even happened.**

I'm so sorry, Raika. The ground was slippery with ice, and it looked to me like you lost your balance and slipped a little.

**I never lose my balance. Ever.**

I know! That's why I think you were caught by surprise. The bad news is that the vet thinks it's that pinched nerve again - remember how that happened to you last year around this time? You probably reinjured that spot. The good news is that the vet said a month of rest should do the trick.

**A month?! Did you fight for my rights? Do you have any idea what that means to a very old dog? A month! I might as well just give up the ghost and expire here and now.**

Raika, I love you so much, and we need to take the time for you to heal so you'll have many more good months ahead of you. So you're staying home for awhile.

**It's going to be hard for you to get a good grade today. Today is not a happy Raika day. You're looking at a D. The only reason it's not an F is because you didn't let the vet take my temperature - who the heck needs a thermometer up their butt when the problem is clearly not in there?**

Well, that's something I guess. At least I passed.

**Would you like to know what it would take to improve your grade?**

I'm not sure.

**How can you say that?! Of course you want to know. This is my quality of life on the line right here. Tell you what. While you are deciding, why don't I just go ahead and tell you?**

I see you're not going to hold back. Fine. What would it take for me to raise my grade?

**I would like a bedtime story.**

Really? Do you have a particular story in mind?

**I want to hear the story of my family: my mom and my dad and my sisters. I know there were five of us, and I know bits and pieces, but I want to hear the whole story from top to bottom!**

I have to get Chris from the train station in a little bit, but we can start now, and then you can take a nap. We'll get to the rest of the story before bed.

**Great! I'm looking forward to it. And good news! I have revised your grade to a B-!**

Well then, good for me!

**Did you want to ask me about your grade, maybe how you could raise it a bit, lest I brand you an underachiever?**

There is absolutely nothing that I want to know about my grade.

**Wow. Underachiever.**

Are you ready for me to start your story?

**I am!**

Okay then, here we go... Once upon a time, there was a dog named Soja, and -

**Soja was my dog mommy right?**

Yes, Raika. Soja was your dog mommy.

**Okay, go ahead.**

All right. So anyway, Soja was pregnant! She was going to -

**Who was the daddy?**

It was YOUR daddy, Reko.

**My dog daddy was named Reko?**

Yes, he was. You are named after him.

**That's cool! I didn't know that.**

So, back to the story. Your mommy was pregnant, and she was going to give birth to you, but we didn't know that yet.

**How come you didn't know?**

Because you weren't here yet, Raika. We couldn't know that you would be you until you arrived.

**Oh. I get it. Okay, go on. Why do you keep stopping?**

Well, your mommy was pregnant and she was all ready to have her babies. So when the time came, we got her special box ready, and Soja got lots of good things to eat because we knew that she would be very hungry for the next few weeks as she was feeding you and your sisters.

**What did you get for her to eat? Did she like duck?**

Raika, we are never going to get to the story of the five sisters if you keep asking questions.

**Sorry. Go on.**

So when the time came, Soja got into her box, and she started having puppies.

**I was the first one!**

Raika! Let me tell the story!

**I almost can't help it. I just got excited, because I used to be a wee little thing!**

Yes, you used to be very tiny. Anyway, four girls came right in a row, and then, a sad thing happened.

**Really?**

Yes. Then there was a little boy, but he died before he had a chance to live.

**Oh, that is sad. I didn't even know I had a brother.**

Yes, you did have a brother. But we never got to know him. And I was feeling a little sad about it when I realized that there was going to be one more puppy! So I tried to stop being sad, and turned back to your mommy to greet the last one.

**Was she the fifth sister?**

Yes, but there's more to the story.

**Well, keep going! Don't keep stopping!**

Raika, you keep stopping me!

**Are we going to argue about this now?**

Are we - ugh, no. Anyway, I saw that there was going to be one more puppy, so I got ready to welcome that puppy to the world.

**And then the fifth puppy was born, right? I bet it was a girl!**

Yes, the fifth puppy was born, and yes, she was a girl. But she was very different from the other puppies. The fifth puppy arrived in her little sac, and I knew right away that something was wrong. She was too small.

**Then what happened?**

I opened up the sac and gave Soja her teeny, tiny puppy. She was about the size of a mouse.

**Oh, that is tiny. Were you excited to have such a tiny puppy? Your own miniature Belgian Tervuren?**

No, Raika. I was scared because I thought she would die.

**But she didn't! Do you know how I know that?**

How do you know that, Raika?

**Because this is the story of the five sisters!**

You're right, Raika. She did live. And actually, she turned into a very special dog.

**More special than me?**

No, Raika. Every puppy in that litter was special. Just like you.

**So then what happened?**

Well, you asked so many questions, that it's way past time for me to go pick up Chris. So I'll have to tell you the rest of the story later. Now… head on pillow… eyes closed… pat, pat, pat... and off you go to sleep. You need rest to get well again!

**You can't stop now!**

Tonight, okay? Head on pillow… eyes closed… pat, pat, pat… and off you go to sleep.

**Good night, Mom.**

Good night, Raika.

## Mom & Raika

Hi Raika, I'm back. How are you holding up?

**Beyond the mind numbing boredom of sitting in the house,**

**looking at the darkness outside my window, and cursing my fate? I'm doing fine.**

Are you ready for the rest of the story of the five sisters?

**Actually, I am. That could potentially brighten this dark and dreary time considerably.**

Well, I'm ready to tell it, too! But I have an idea.

**What's that?**

How about if you save your questions until the end so that we can get all the way through the story?

**But what if I forget one of my questions? Then I'll be awake all night trying to remember it. And then I'll remember at 3 A.M., so I'll have to wake you up and ask you the question right then, so I don't forget it again... which is fine, I suppose, since you say I wake up all night and walk the house like a ghost anyway, so no skin off my nose. Okay. I'll wait until the end for my questions.**

On second thought, perhaps you should ask your questions at the exact moment that they occur to you.

**Okay, that works, too!**

Anyway, we left off with the birth of the last puppy, a very tiny, wee one.

**I was the red puppy, I remember! I assume that was because of my amazing mahogany color? Even at birth you could see my lovely highlights?**

Not exactly. Each puppy was given a collar so that we could tell you apart. We had blue puppy, pink puppy, green puppy, and red puppy - and you are right, that was you.

**But that's only four puppies.**

That's true. We didn't give Little a collar since it was pretty obvious which one she was.

**You called her Little?**

Yeah. That seemed pretty reasonable, don't you think?

**I guess it does. So what happened next?**

It was nighttime, so I went to bed. I was due to deliver a baby myself in a few weeks and I was hoping to get some sleep before my time came. But I was worried. I took one last look at all of you, and finally I forced myself to head for bed. I stayed away for a couple of hours.

**Then what happened?**

I couldn't sleep no matter what I tried. So I came back to look at the puppies again.

**Were we all okay?**

No, not this time. Four of you were nursing away and looking very healthy. But the littlest one - she was all by herself in a corner, and Soja wasn't paying any attention to her. I think she had given up on her tiny baby.

**What did you do?**

I took her out of the box and got a wee, tiny bottle with a wee, tiny nipple attached, and I tried to give her something to eat.

**Oh, good! That was a good idea! Did she enjoy her meal?**

Well, no. She was too weak to suck on the nipple. So I got a special tube that went into her stomach, filled it up with puppy milk, and gave her that.

**Did Soja appreciate your help?**

I'm not sure. But between feedings, Little stayed with the rest of you, and Soja took care of her as well.

**So then what happened?**

Well, for the next three days, I fed her every two hours. She held her own. She was small, but she was strong! She just wasn't quite big enough to manage on her own. And then one day, I went to feed Little, and I found her nursing with the rest of you. I never had to feed her again.

**Wow, that's great! Did she catch up in size?**

No, she never caught up. She was always quite a bit smaller, but you know what?

**What?**

I just looked at the clock, and it's way past your bedtime. You need lots of sleep so you can heal. We'll finish this story tomorrow.

**Mom, I want to hear the rest of the story!!**

And I will tell you the rest of the story after you've had a good sleep.

**Your grade is slipping to a high C, you know.**

I believe that. Nevertheless. Head on pillow. Eyes closed. Raika, eyes closed! Good. Now... pat, pat, pat and off to sleep.

**Since when do I get mistreated like this? We're in the middle of a story!**

Good night Raika.

**A high D!**

Head on pillow. Eyes closed, Raika. Now.

**Not okay.**

Sleep tight, Raika.

## Mom & Raika

Hi, Raika. I'm not sure if I should ask if you're having a nice day.

**Go ahead and ask. It might take thirty minutes to get through my thoughts on this crappy day.**

Are you in pain?

**Nope. The vet seems to have thought of everything, except for my slowly dwindling will to live.**

Maybe the final installment of your bedtime story will distract you a bit.

**That might create something of a bright spot. And it better be the whole thing tonight, because it looks to me like you are trying to take advantage of my cooperative nature by drawing it out the way you are.**

Cooperative nature. Cough, cough. Excuse me. There must be something caught in my throat. When did you ever have a cooperative nature?

**My whole life! You said, "Jump!" and I said, "How high?" And now - now that I'm trying to assert a little control over my own existence, you accuse me of being uncooperative, and you try to take advantage of me!**

I will finish the whole story. Okay?

**Promise?**

I do. I promise. The whole rest of the story of the five sisters, coming right up.

**All right. Go ahead, then.**

Well, then. Once Little had joined the rest of you, and I had stopped worrying so much, life went back to normal, for the most part. You grew up together and did the things that puppies do. You played and barked and squabbled, and in general, you made a lot of trouble for our human family and your doggy mommy.

**I bet Soja was an amazing mommy!**

Nope! She was terrible.

**No way! I was a wonderful mother. How could Soja not have been a wonderful mother, too?**

It is true that you were an extremely attentive and protective mother. But your dog mommy was not. After about two days, she was done with motherhood. She wanted to go back to working and playing with me. I had a terrible time getting her to take proper care of all of you.

**That's terrible! What did you do?**

Well, remember how I said I was pregnant? That was Chris. He was born just a few weeks after you were. So what worked for us was everyone sitting together, and Soja and I nursed our babies together. As long as I wasn't moving, she was willing to stay in the whelping box and nurse all of you. It worked out.

**Are you saying that my dog mommy didn't love me?**

Not at all, Raika. It's just that your mom was more of a working-mom type than a stay-at-home type. She was perfectly kind to you, only she didn't want to be tied down, so her maternity leave was rather short, at her request. Cleaning up after baby puppies just wasn't her thing.

**So then we all grew up?**

Yep, you all grew up. Your names were your collar colors, except for the little puppy, of course. And boy did she get a lot of attention. When it came to getting her way, she held her own. She was small, but tough!

**Where did the other puppies go?**

You stayed here with me, of course, and became well known as an obedience dog, among your other accomplishments. The blue puppy became Kesa, and she went to Arizona where she developed into a very talented agility dog. The pink puppy became Emmy, and she went to Southern California where she performed very well in lots of different sports, but she was famous for her nosework. Now, the green puppy became Pico, and she went to New York. She broke all kinds of records as a dock diving dog - she even got invited to be on TV!

**Wow, really? On TV? That's kind of cool. I bet I could have done all of those things.**

You did do most of those things, Raika. I hope you remember that.

**And what happened to the little one?**

Little went to Wisconsin where she became a great agility dog. Her grown-up name was Thrill. She was never very big, but she sure was fast! Even the border collies knew she could beat them, if she remembered to listen to her mom. She did struggle with the listening part.

**Must be genetic.**

That crossed my mind, too.

**Could we have a reunion?**

Raika, you all got older. It's too late for that.

**Did all of my sisters die?**

No. Emmy is still here, just like you. And that makes us very, very happy.

**Me too. I like being here. So is that the whole story?**

Yes, that is the story of the five sisters.

**You're not holding anything back to spring on me when I'm least expecting it?**

No, I don't think so. That's the whole story.

**Thanks for telling me the story.**

You're welcome. Now, it's bedtime. What has to happen?

**You start a new story!**

Raika.

**No new story?**

Raika, must you always give me grief?

**I was thinking it was closer to enthusiasm than grief, but I get your point.**

What has to happen?

**Head on pillow. Eyes closed. Pat, pat, pat... and off to sleep?**

Exactly right. Head on pillow. Eyes closed. Pat, pat, pat and off to sleep! Good night.

**See you in the morning.**

### Raika & Mom

**I have a question.**

What's your question, Raika?

**Why did you keep me? Out of the five puppies... why me?**

Are you asking for another bedtime story? I know this has been a rough time for you, locked in the house with not much to do but sleep to pass the time.

**This isn't a bedtime story. It's just a question.**

All right. Let me think for a moment. It was a long, long time ago, you know.

**But you can remember, right?**

Yes, I remember.

**Tell me, then.**

I wanted a dog who would enjoy participating in dog sports with me.

**How could you tell if one of us five sisters would be better at that than another? All of us ran around as fast as we could, and played and climbed and had tugging contests. Why me?**

You were different, Raika. You watched me all the time. You stayed near and waited for me to notice while your siblings raced around the yard, tumbling all over each other. You were calm, and you kept your eyes on me, so I guess my answer is that I didn't pick you. You picked me.

# Part Two

## Chapter 33:
## Raika Saves Nick's Life

Raika & Mom
<hr>

**Mom, I have a surprise for you.**

Really? What is it?

**You have to guess. I'll give you five guesses.**

Hmm. Let's see. You found a way to climb onto the counter and ate the meat that was defrosting in the sink?

**No, Mom, of course not. I have way too much arthritis for that - plus this stupid pinched nerve thing. Although if I were physically able to get up there... not a bad idea. Take another guess!**

Uh... you emptied the trash all over the floor and I need to pick it up?

**No way. If I empty the trash, I shred the paper parts to remind you that paper should be put in the recycling bin or in my wastepaper basket.**

Right. Well. I'm on my third guess now?

**Right.**

You stole my phone, scheduled an Uber, and arranged for a field day at the park?

**You know, if I were the fragile sort, I might be offended by your sarcasm.**

That's true. Sorry. I'll try harder now, okay?

**All right; you have two more guesses.**

Gee. No clue. Seriously, I'm stumped.

**For real?  You have no ideas at all, none?**

Well, no.  All of the ideas that occur to me may possibly be a teeny bit offensive.  And now I feel the need to walk through the house and just take a quick peek around...

**Mom, the house is fine.  How about if I just tell you, instead?  Are you ready?**

Yes, I'm ready.  What's the surprise?

**I'm going to tell YOU a bedtime story!**

Hey, that's great!  Do I get to pick the topic?

**Um.  Well.  What do you want me to tell you about?**

Tell me a story about how I'm the best mom in the whole world.

**That's kind of hard.  Maybe something a little easier for my first story?**

You're kidding.  You can't tell me a story about how great a mom I am?

**Well.  I mean... I could.  It's just... sometimes you could do more...**

Fine.  I am not offended.  Even though I absolutely am.  Okay, you pick the topic.  What would you like your story to be about?

**How about I give you three options, all true stories, and you pick the one you like best?**

All right.  What are my choices?

**I could tell the story of when I saved our family from burning up in the fire, or how I saved Brito from drowning in the pool, or how I stopped your friend from beating up Nick.**

Are you sure these are all nonfiction?

**Maybe only one of them.**

One of those is nonfiction? Where was I when it happened?

**Right here with me. But you missed the whole thing. Completely oblivious.**

Which one might that be?

**When your friend almost beat up Nick!**

I don't remember that story so that sounds like a winner. I'm ready.

**Well, now you have to wait until tomorrow. We've run out of time.**

You have got to be joking.

**Nope. Now you know how it feels.**

Well, then. I'm going to set a good example for you and cooperate. So tomorrow night, I'll look forward to hearing your story.

**Great! It's a date. Now then... head on pillow... eyes closed... pat, pat, pat and off to sleep!**

Good night, Raika. I'm really looking forward to hearing the story of how you saved Nick from being beaten up.

## Raika & Mom

**Hi, Mom. Did you have a snack?**

I did!

**Did you have a drink? Maybe a glass of wine?**

I did!

**Or maybe two?**

Raika, what's your point?

**Just want to make sure you're comfortable.**

I'm comfortable. Is it time for my story?

**It is. Today I will tell you the story called "Raika Saves Nick's Life."**

You saved Nick's life? I thought you said you saved him from a beating.

**Sometimes people don't recover from beatings. So for all we know, I saved his life. However, if you keep asking questions, we might not finish the whole story.**

Okay, so tell me the story about you saving Nick's life.

**Once upon a time, when I was a much younger dog, some lady friends of yours came to visit. They seemed nice, but in fact, they were violent people and you seemed completely unaware of that.**

Might these ladies have had names?

**Mmmm... don't remember. But maybe you could stop interrupting me.**

Sorry. Go on.

**As I was saying, there were two ladies staying at the house with us. I recall you sitting at the kitchen table with one of the ladies, examining the contents of a large box. Something about dog food that didn't look very appealing? While you were trying to figure out what to do with it, the other lady was talking to Nick. But you couldn't see that because you were facing the other way. It looked like they were having a good time, but still I was keeping an eye on the situation because that's what good dogs do.**

Now that you mention it, I actually do remember that box of dog food. That's a whole story unto itself. And now I think I know where this story might be going.

**You really need to work on your interrupting problem, Mom. Anyway, as I was saying before I was interrupted - again - you were trying to figure out what to do with the contents of the box, and the other lady was talking to Nick while I supervised them. And then, totally out of the blue, she tried to hit him!**

Raika, that's not really -

**Stop interrupting! We'll never finish this story the way we're going right now!**

But Raika -

**MOM!!**

Fine. Continue.

**Well, when I saw what was happening, I leapèd between Nick and the lady as quick as lightning, jumped into the air, clacked my jaws together an inch from her face, and let out a big roar! My job done, I sat between them to monitor the situation. By the time you turned around, that's all you saw: Raika sitting politely between Nick and the violent lady. With me on guard, Nick could never be threatened again, even if you weren't paying attention. So there it is, Mom. The story of how I saved Nick's life. Pretty good story, no?**

Yes, it's a great story! But Raika, there's something I need to tell you.

**What's that?**

The lady wasn't going to hit Nick. She was pretending. Play fighting. People do it, too.

**No, Mom. I don't think so. She raised her hand just like she was going to hit him.**

Yes, Raika. I was right there listening to the conversation between the two of them. There was no conflict there, no threat. You misunderstood.

**But all of these years, I thought I had saved Nick from being assaulted...**

Don't feel bad, Raika, because you know what? Until that day, I didn't really believe that you would defend our family when it mattered. No offense, but I tend to think of you as a fun and sporty dog rather than a serious one. But after that day, I knew that you would always try to keep us safe.

**Of course I would. I'm astonished that you would doubt me!**

It's not that I doubted you, Raika. It's just that no one knows for sure what they will do in an emergency until they have to face it head-on. And you truly believed that there was a threat. You read it wrong, but that's not the point. You thought there was real danger, and you responded. Do you want to know what surprised me the most, Raika?

**That I didn't actually remove the lady's nose?**

Nope. The part that surprised me the most is that you've always ignored the kids. You're my dog. You've always been my dog. Until then, I didn't know if you really cared about anyone else.

**Mom. We're a family. It's my job to take care of the whole family, not to worry about who I do or do not like. Dogs don't work that way.**

Well, just so you know, my respect for you grew a lot that day. You were courageous and sensible. I was impressed.

**So was it still a good story? Even though maybe it didn't happen the way I thought it did?**

In my mind, it's an even better story.

**But now I don't feel like such a heroine anymore.**

Well, Raika, we can never know for sure what would have happened... maybe, just maybe, my friend had turned into a psychopath for five seconds, and you did indeed save Nick's life.

**I like that possibility. Let's run with that.**

Let's.

**Now, Mom? It's time for you to go to bed.**

I am awfully tired, maybe you're right.

**Head on pillow. Close eyes. Pat, pat, pat and off to sleep!**

Thank you Raika. Maybe you, too? Head on pillow. Close eyes. Pat, pat, pat and off to sleep with you!

**Good night, Mom.**

Good night, Raika.

## Raika & Mom

**It's over?**

Yes, Raika, it's over. You're free to resume your regular life without restrictions, except for a gradual return to full activity.

**I cannot believe I just gave up a month of my life laying on my dog bed with not much more than stories and paper shredding to keep me busy. I don't have that much life left to be wasting it like that.**

It's over now. We're keeping a couple of the medicines around just in case the pain comes back, but otherwise it's time to resume our normal routine. And with spring right around the corner, I'd say the future looks pretty good!

# Part Two

Chapter 34:
Molecular Redistribution

## Raika & Mom

**When I go through my molecular redistribution, I am going to give Brito my quietness.**

Your what?

**My quietness. He makes too much noise.**

No, not that part, the first part.

**My molecular redistribution?**

Yeah, that part. Raika, I'm not following.

**When my molecules get redistributed wherever they are needed, I will give Brito my quiet voice. He sure needs it. And I think I will give Lyra my loyalty so she can help take care of you.**

I have no idea what you're talking about.

**You don't remember your molecular acquisition day?**

No, I don't. You've lost me completely.

**Well, right before I was born, I got my personality molecules. My emotions, my habits, my clever nature - little things like that. All the things that make me unique.**

You did?

**Of course. Didn't that happen to you right before you were born?**

I have no idea. I cannot remember the time before I was born.

**I don't mean a full memory - more the feeling of it. Don't**

you remember when you got your new molecules right
before your birth?

I don't think so? Tell me more.

Well, molecular acquisition day was probably the most
exciting day of my life! As each new group of molecules
showed up, I became a bit more - well, me! I found out
that I was going to be witty and sharp and an amazing
problem solver. I also knew that I was going to be a little
bossy. That's why I pushed my way to the front of the line
and was born first; I had to show my littermates the way
out. There's never any time to waste in getting started on
your destiny!

Well, this is certainly new. Where did your molecules come from?

From other dogs that had passed on. When they died,
their personality molecules got redistributed wherever
they were needed.

So redistributed molecules go to puppies?

Not necessarily. For example, if an adult dog is grumpy,
and if he is working on self-improvement, then he might
get a cheerful molecule to help with his grumpiness even
though he's all grown up. Of course, the distribution
that happens right before birth is the big one that sets
the stage, but the distribution process never truly ends.
That's why we can grow and change. Basically, the
redistribution keeps all of the personality traits of the
world in balance.

I can't believe you never told me this before. So that's what happens
after you die? You go through a molecular redistribution? And you
give all of your personality molecules to wherever they are needed?

I can't say that I know exactly how the process works
because my time hasn't come yet. I know how we get them
because I remember the feeling of them entering my body,

**but not how we give them away. But when the time comes, I'll give you a few molecules, too.**

You can give me your molecules?

**I believe so. I think you might need some small bits of me to help you with the sadness you'll be feeling, and to make sure you stay engaged with the world even after I'm gone. And I'll request that they be lodged directly in your heart, so you'll feel me near... Mom, are you crying? Don't cry!**

Of course I'm crying - you just told me the most amazing thing! I need to wrap my head around this a bit.

**Maybe a walk in the fresh air would help with your thinking?**

Yes, that's probably a good plan. And Raika?

**Yeah?**

You're right. When the time comes, I'm going to need those molecules. Probably a lot of them. So don't forget, okay? Because I lied. I am not crying just because you told me about molecular distribution. I am crying because I know I am going to feel a very deep sadness, and I won't know how to manage the pain. I'll want to stay home and disengage from life altogether - lose myself in work or random goals again.

**I won't forget. Mom, it's good that you're talking about it. It's time for us to talk about dying - how I'm going to leave this world.**

We can start talking about it.

**I'm having this vaguely opportunistic feeling that this might be a good time to start those discussions**

Dammit, Raika. I lied again. I'm not ready to talk about you dying.

**But you will be eventually?**

Yes, I will. So how about you talk and I listen? That might be the best way to get started.

**We have a deal. On a related topic, I wonder if there's a way to give Brito some of my quiet molecules now, before I pass. I wish I had a way to find out beforehand.**

# Chapter 35:
## Getting Old Deserves a Conversation

## Mom & Raika

Raika, I have a new treat for you to try!

**Oooh! What flavor?**

I'm not sure. Give it a try.

**Hmm... it doesn't smell quite right. No, thank you. You can give it to the other dogs.**

Well, it's actually especially for you.

**I appreciate the thought.**

So I'd like you to eat it.

**Mom, appreciating the thought doesn't make it tasty. What else do you have?**

You see, Raika, there's more to it than that. This treat will help you with your peeing problem. There are pills inside. The old pills don't help anymore, so we're trying something new. But the only way to know if they help is if you take them.

**I am not enjoying this conversation.**

I understand, Raika. Someday I am going to be old, and I suspect I'll be leaking pee at the wrong times, too. That's just the way it is. It's better to address it now, instead of winding up with serious health problems if we don't get this under control.

**Getting old is hard.**

Yes, getting old is hard. Let's make it as good as possible, okay?

**Yeah, but I won't eat the pill. So you're going to have to**

**find a way to make it go down, and as the human with the
big brain, I'll leave it to you to figure that out.**

That's fair. One more thing about the peeing?

**More? I'm trying to imagine what you could possibly
have to add to the fact that I'm peeing in the house.**

Well, something a little strange happened this morning. Didn't see it
for myself, but Dad told me about it.

**What happened?**

Dad said he got you up at the normal time and went to take you
outside. But he got distracted in the kitchen for a minute, and when
he turned around to open the door, he watched you empty your entire
bladder on your dog bed.

**That didn't happen! I don't remember that at all.**

Well, Dad said he was kind of shocked. So shocked that he just
stood there and watched as you finished. Then you walked away, and
when he went to check, indeed you had emptied your entire bladder
on your bed instead of going outside. So we're thinking maybe you
were sleepwalking? And you just got a little confused and thought
you were outside but you were still in the house? We're not making
a big deal out of it or anything, but it was... odd. And I'm a little
concerned that it might be an extension of the other problems you're
having at night. You don't remember those, either.

**I see. Is there anything good that comes with getting old?**

Yes. You're still here with me. And that is worth everything.

## Raika & Mom

**Mom?**

Yes, Raika?

**How will you know when it's time for me to die?**

What do you mean?

**Well, someday my life won't be very good anymore. It won't be worth living. That's when it will be my time to die, right? So how will you know?**

I don't know. I'm hoping that someday, at the right time, you'll just go to sleep and not wake up.

**How often have you heard of that happening with dogs?**

Not very often, I suppose.

**You promised we could start talking about this soon. When will you be ready?**

I don't know.

**We need to.**

Why?

**Because sometimes when it's time for dogs to die, the owners aren't prepared to make the most important decisions. I don't want that to happen to us. I'm going to be fifteen this year!**

Mmmm.

**Mom? Mom!**

I think it's still too soon to have this conversation.

**No. It's not. These are exactly the conversations we need to be having. I'm not asking to be put to sleep. I'm asking you to think now about how you will decide. Now is the best time to think about it, when it isn't... well... a matter of life and death.**

What if we approach it a little differently? Why don't you tell me what it would take for you to not want to be here anymore.

**Okay. I'll do that. I'll get back to you. And Mom? You have no idea how much it means to me that you're listening. This is important. You're going to be making the decisions at the end of my life when I cannot. I'll need you to be there, and to be strong, when you most want to advocate for yourself. When the time comes, it has to be about me and not about you, and I'm going to need your help. To make this happen, I need you to start talking to me. Soon. I need to know that you will be ready and able to do what is right for me when you will be at your weakest.**

**And while you think about that, I'm going to think about what you have asked - what would it take for me not to want to be here anymore - and I will come back with an answer. Because you're right, the answer to that question is fundamental to everything that happens between us as we go forward into uncharted territory.**

## Mom

I worry. I worry all the time. I worry when she wakes up at night and wanders around like a ghost. I worry when she sleeps deeply; maybe she's passed and I didn't even know it. I worry when she pants; is it pain? I worry when she struggles to walk in a straight line. I worry about her appetite; even a single missed meal makes me worry. I need to prepare myself for the inevitable, and I worry about that, too!

Then the next day rolls around and she's doing amazing! Running around strong and fit, eating all of her meals, and begging for more!

There will be an end, I know that. Lord knows she wants to discuss it, and then everything changes again. A good day. A bad day. A terrible day, and then a spectacular one! How am I supposed to "get ready" when my emotions are tied to a living creature with no linear path to... anywhere?

I ignore it as best I can, that worry. We walk and I think, "What can go wrong with a dog who can walk four miles?" I feel indulgent with my old dog doddering along, happy and doing well, enjoying life, taking full advantage of every opportunity. I ignore that the story has to end. That's what I do most days. Worry and ignore.

But then some days come around and I can't pretend. I see a mortal dog. I see pain and anxiety. I see change. And then she's not a cute-old dog; she's a sick-old dog facing the end of her life. I think about the decisions that are ahead, the things that she wants to talk about - and that I want to ignore. When the time comes, how will I make the right decisions?

On a fundamental level, the question is simple: how will I know when it is time for her to die? Which has nothing in common with the question I want to ask, which is, "How will I let go when it's time for her to die?" And yet, if I do not start with the first question, then the second one will invariably keep her here - with nothing left to live for - well past the point where compassion demands action.

So maybe there is a third question for me to focus on: "How might I ensure that the end of her life is really about her, and not about me?"

## Raika

**She's listening.**

**It's time to talk about the bigger picture, and the bigger picture is not life. It's death.**

**I'm not complaining about the pills. I'm not complaining about the pain. I'm not complaining about my life - I love my life, and I know I need help to stay here, happy and comfortable. I don't want to leave Mom, ever. But the time will come, and we need to talk about it now.**

**Death. I will leave my body behind, and my molecules will go where they're needed. I can accept the unknown; it's okay. I want Mom to love me and hear me for as long as**

possible. I know she can love me; she loves me more each day. Now it's time to be heard.

And therein lies the problem. If she hears and understands, then she must let me go when it is right for me, not when it is right for her.

People say the ultimate sacrifice is losing one's own life, but they are wrong. The ultimate sacrifice is taking the life of another - one who is truly loved - because that is the right thing to do.

And that is what I am asking for. When the time is right.

# Spring 2019

## Chapter 36:
### Mrs. Mountain Lion

### Mom & Raika

Raika, every time we walk, you smell that rock. There must be twenty other rocks here, but you always head straight for that one. What's so special about it?

**Maybe you should smell it for yourself?**

My guess is that all I'd smell is dog pee since one presumes other dogs have peed here.

**You really don't smell it?**

I really don't, Raika.

**That is where the mountain lion was. I'm just fascinated by it. So each time I come by, I smell it again to see if maybe the future has arrived a little differently than I expected. I want to see if things are the same as always, or if maybe Mrs. Mountain Lion has changed her schedule or moved on to other parts.**

A mountain lion? Walked by this rock?

**Well, it's more than that. She rubs back and forth on the rock.**

And you can smell that?

**Definitely. It's pretty hard to miss, actually.**

What does it smell like, Raika?

**It smells like... a mountain lion rubbing herself back and forth on a rock! Really, I have no way to explain to you what smell is like. How would you describe what you can see to a person who has never had sight? I can say that it changes and shifts and settles all around me. When I walk through a new area, the first thing I do is take in the smells, just like the first thing you do is take in the sights. The difference is that I can tell what has happened in the past as well as the present, whereas you can only see what is there right now. I don't think you can see the past, can you?**

No, I cannot see the past.

**So I guess that's different, isn't it? The reason I come back to this rock each day is because I cannot smell the future, so this gives me something to look forward to on our walks.**

It must be frustrating for you when I'm in a hurry and I make you move past everything that might be really interesting.

**It is frustrating. Probably a lot like driving past the Grand Canyon with an impatient blind person who is in no mood for dawdling. Regardless, I'm really sorry you can't smell very much. That seems like a terrible handicap.**

You know, Raika, you're right. There is a whole way to experience the world that isn't - and never will be - open to me. However, I promise that from this day forward, I will really try to make sure it is fully open to you as much as I can. We will walk at your speed so you can sniff along as we go, taking in the smells as you wish.

**I would love that, Mom. Thank you for understanding.**

## Raika & Mom

**Time for bed, Mom!**

I know I go to bed early, but it's not even 9 P.M. That's a bit early, even by my standards.

**Yes, but I'm tired now, so off to bed we go!**

You can go without me.

**No, I can't! There will be no one to keep an eye on you.**

Really, you need to go to bed. You're bothering me.

**That's because you're ignoring me!**

I'm not ignoring you; I'm telling you to go to bed on your own and I'll be there soon.

**That simply won't work for me. So I will huff and puff and climb on you until you pay attention.**

How about you sleep under the desk until it's time to go to bed so Dad and I finish up our movie?

**That's what I do during the day. Now it's time to go for a real night's sleep! Then we can see what the morning will bring.**

How about just a little rest under the desk? We'll go to bed soon.

**How long are you thinking? Five minutes or so?**

Maybe just a bit more?

**Okay. I'll rest here for five minutes on the cold tile floor while you watch TV. Then we can negotiate again.**

Excellent, Raika.

**Excellent!**

**So... it's been four minutes, which is close to five. I'd say it's time for bed.**

Raika, I have a new trick for you to learn; how about we turn this into a training session?

**What's the trick?**

It's called "Put yourself to bed and stay there all night."

**That doesn't seem like a trick.**

Sure it is - if you do a good job. So now that you are starting to feel sleepy, you'll head down the hallway into the bedroom, hop up on your bed, and go to sleep! Then I'll join you just a little bit later when the movie is over, and we will wake up together in the morning.

**That sounds terrible! I want us both to go right now.**

I know about dogs who do just that! When they get sleepy, they trot down the hallway all by themselves and head right to bed - and they stay put!

**Who watches over their owners? I mean, what if you had a heart attack or something and no one was there to tell the tale?**

I'd like to believe you would be more interested in getting me some help than just telling the tale, but regardless, there are other humans around most of the time. Plus, Dad is sitting here with me right now.

**You would give the teenagers responsibility for your life?**

I was putting my money on Dad.

**I see. Well, I think that's a terrible plan. I am a herding dog, and we don't abdicate responsibility so easily. Maybe those other dogs were hounds or terriers or something. You know, the kind of dogs that are used to running off after prey and just abandoning people to whatever fate**

**might befall them.**

Maybe.

**Anyway, maybe what we need is a routine that we can count on.  Maybe 8 P.M. for PJs and washing up?  Then off to bed at 8:30 on the dot!**

No new trick?

**No new trick.**

# Part Two

Chapter 37:
Wandering Raika

## Mom & Raika

You kept me up all night, and I'm not even traveling anymore. I stopped that entirely, remember?

> **Are you referring to my gentle attempts to check on you? I can't help it! I need to make sure you're still breathing. Every time I wake up, I think about it, and I get a little panicky until I know that everything is okay. I like my routines, you know.**

You know I'm still breathing. I look at you every time you poke me. You still poke!

> **Unless you pat my head, I cannot be sure. Do you see how nicely I go back to sleep after you pat my head?**

Yes, I do see that. It doesn't last very long though, because now you wander around the house staring at walls. When did that even start? It's every few nights now - another round of "Wandering Raika."

> **Paralysis can come on slowly. So as I lie on my bed, I start to worry that it could have happened to you, so I check on you.**

Well, it doesn't make for a very restful night. And why did you avoid my question about your nighttime behavior - the wandering part?

> **I know exactly what you mean; it's not restful at all! I was exhausted from working so hard.**

You were? At one point you slept so hard that when you started dreaming, I literally thought you were having a seizure. You were kicking every which way and I couldn't wake you up!

> **I don't remember that. And how do you reconcile such**

a deep sleep with this supposed wandering through the
house?

You tell me.

So what happened in my deep sleep?

Well, for one or two minutes, your whole body was twitching.
Scared the crap out of me. I was talking to you and petting you and
nothing - you didn't wake up. And then finally I thumped you kind
of hard on your side and you came flying up. You were totally clear
and awake.

Wow, how scary!

It was scary.

So did you check on me for the rest of the night? Make
sure I was alive? That's what I would have done for sure.

I didn't have to. You went back to checking on me. There was no
doubt that you were alive.

Good thing. If anything happens to me, there won't be
anyone checking on you.

So then, Raika? This other thing is happening, and I'd like to ask
you about it.

What's that?

Well, in addition to wandering around the house, you're getting stuck
in corners.

I don't think I understand. How does one get stuck in a
corner?

That's the part that confuses me. You seem to be stuck. All you
have to do is turn around, but you don't. You wait for me to turn
you around. I've seen it a few times now. I wasn't paying too much
attention at first, but then last night I realized it was becoming a
pattern. You wander around somewhere, and then I don't hear you

walking anymore. When I check, you're not in your bed, either. So I go looking for you, and I find you staring into a corner, seemingly unable to get out.

**I don't know, Mom. You tell me these things, but I don't remember them. And it doesn't sound like anyone's getting hurt, so we should probably just ignore it.**

For a dog who spends so much energy trying to talk about death and dying, you sure aren't a fan of this particular topic of conversation.

**I find this conversation more than a little uncomfortable and definitely not important. Plus, since I don't remember it, I cannot be sure that it is happening the way that you're saying.**

I don't lie to you.

**I didn't say you were lying. Just that maybe I would interpret the situation differently. Let's talk about something else now. For example, I get lonely when you leave the house, even if it's not for a whole weekend. Sometimes even a little panicky. So could you try not to leave me alone in the house too much? It's okay if it's just Dad or one of the kids, but I don't like to be completely alone.**

I'll try, Raika. That could be a little tricky because we all go out together sometimes, but at the very least I'll leave Lyra for company, okay?

**Yeah, I guess that would be okay. She's kind of growing on me.**

After eight years, she's growing on you?

**Some things take time. She's one of those things.**

Part Two

## Chapter 38:
### Skunks and Early Walks

### Mom & Raika

Raika? You sure got some explaining to do.

**I know! Let me tell you what happened.**

I'm listening.

**I thought I heard a commotion in the backyard, so I went outside to see what was happening. Well, much to my surprise, I saw Lyra and Brito being attacked by a skunk! With no thought to my personal safety, I sprang into action! Unfortunately, as I came up behind to grab it by the neck, it sprayed me in the face.**

The skunk was attacking? You sprang into action? I know you're amazingly fit for your age, but... you sprang?

**Yes, can you believe that?**

Well. No.

**Well, seeing as you were not there, do you have a better explanation?**

I was thinking that you went outside to pee, didn't hear the skunk warn you because your hearing and eyesight have gone to hell in a handbasket, and as a result you tripped over the skunk and got sprayed in the face.

**That seems a little far-fetched. Did you want to hear my alternative story about how the skunk suddenly leapt up and flew through the air, baring its teeth and coming right at me? Honestly, I liked that one better, but I was a little concerned you would make me go to the vet for a check**

**up. Plus, I wasn't sure how to reconcile the fact that the teeth and the butt are on opposite ends.**

Good thing you didn't use that story. I know how you feel about the vet.

**Yeah, good thing.**

You know, you're also very lucky that you're old, because if this had happened to one of the other dogs, I would've left them outside until I felt like giving them a bath. Early morning baths are not my idea of a good time. And after that bath, I would've left them in the garage until they got dry enough to come in the house, rather than blow drying them and following it up with a walk.

**Speaking of which, today's walk was not as good as it could have been. You get a C.**

You're kidding, right? I'm out there against my will and you're giving me a C?

**You were hurrying me along; I felt very pressured. I was trying to eat the fresh grass and do a bit of sniffing, but you kept calling me. This could be my last year of spring grass, you know. And you promised, remember? More sniffing walks?**

I was trying to keep moving so I could stay warm.

**Did you think to bring a warm jacket?**

I brought a jacket, but not the warm one - it's supposed to be spring!

**Well then.**

I was cold, but if we just kept moving, I would get warm enough.

**But I didn't get to sniff the smells and eat the fresh grass!**

I know, but you still had the full four miles to explore. Plus, sometimes you get carried away with that grass, and then you vomit. And let's not forget why we were even out there in the first place!

**Still a C.**

## Raika & Mom

**Mom, Lyra just stole a piece of my packing paper! One of the pieces I had already pulled off!**

Raika, it looks like you still have twelve feet of packing paper left. That tiny little piece that Lyra took doesn't matter.

**It does matter. Today she takes four inches, tomorrow she takes four yards!**

I don't think Lyra is that kind of dog.

**Wait - did you see that? She ate it! She ate my paper! She may not have been that kind of dog before, but look at her now! She's totally out of line!**

Raika. It was a tiny piece.

**But now she'll want more! Next thing you know, she'll be demanding her own packing paper to shred.**

Well, at least that would keep her busy. Then you wouldn't have to wonder if she was getting something you didn't get - you would know she had the same thing as you.

**Is that supposed to make me feel better? Because it doesn't.**

I think you should work on your sharing skills.

**I think you should work on your supervision skills!**

So here's a thought. Remember when you told me that she was growing on you? I wonder if you could hasten your friendship a bit by being a little more generous with her. Maybe then she would be more generous with you. I've noticed she stays nearby now when I'm about to leave the house; maybe you could give a little something in return.

**Ah. I will think about that. Maybe I can give her a little packing paper. Eh - probably not, but I need to think about this more. I don't like to share.**

I know, Raika. It's going to be okay. And Raika? I owe you an apology about the other day. I promised you more sniffing walks, but when it ended up being a cold day, I started hurrying you along again. That wasn't right. I will do better going forward, I promise. I owe you that. If I get cold, how about I walk in circles around you? That will warm me right up!

**Sounds good! And since you're awake early today, how about we go for a walk right now?**

Raika, it's 8 A.M. We never go for a walk this early.

**Now that I think about it, I bet the smells are different. You know, with the lower temperature and higher moisture? There may be whole new things for me to explore! Sadly, probably a little less for you.**

Well, for starters, by the time afternoon comes around, you will have forgotten that we went. And then you will want to go again.

**Not seeing the problem.**

I see the problem. I can only do so much walking. I get tired!

**Mom, do you really want to tell your almost fifteen-year-old dog that you can't keep up?**

Fifteen. You had to remind me. Not that I've forgotten; I think about your age pretty much every day.

**You know, you really don't do enough during the day, though I give you credit for your newfound efforts at family time in the evening. But during the day, you just tap away at that computer. That's a lot of sitting, which probably isn't good for your circulation. Now compare that to me. I have to keep the dogs in line around here in addition to maintaining my health regimen. You've got**

**it good! The more I think about it, the more I think we should go for our morning walk right now, and then add that afternoon walk as soon as you say it's afternoon. You know, Mom? We should make it a regular staple of our exercise plan!**

"Our" exercise plan? So we've gone from discussing whether or not we should have an early morning walk today to an ongoing tradition? When did that happen?

**Traditions have to start somewhere. We can go for our morning walk, go for our afternoon walk, and then wrap up the day with one last walk if I forget the first ones.**

With bedtime at 8:30?

**The future is looking so promising!**

Part Two

Chapter 39:
Sleepless Nights

## Mom & Raika

Raika, don't start eating toilet paper in the middle of the night. Your night wandering is weird enough without adding the bathroom to your rounds.

**Why not?**

I don't even know where to start. First, at night you're supposed to be sleeping. So sleep. Second, if you actually figure out how to get to the end of the toilet paper and pull, you're going to make a huge mess. And third, toilet paper is not for eating.

**Maybe I just get bored at night. I need more to do! Do you have something for me to do? Plus, you forgot to give me a bedtime snack, so I was a little bit hungry.**

Listen to what I said. You're supposed to be sleeping. And does this mean you still don't remember your nighttime escapades? Not even a glimmer?

**Listen to my response. Sleeping is boring. And nope! Still don't remember. But I'm sharp as a tack during the day. Ask me a question from the past - anything! I will wow you with my memory.**

Sleeping is neither exciting or boring. It's relaxing! That's what allows your body to recover from your day.

**I bet that's it right there! I'm not getting enough exercise during the day. I think that's the problem.**

I don't know, Raika. I was actually thinking of cutting back on your exercise a little. The last few days you've really been dragging on the last part coming home.

**I'm so glad you noticed! Now I have to figure out how to get the cars driving by to notice. You know, so they can stop and offer me a ride up the driveway?**

Is this conversation in any way related to your attempts to eat toilet paper at night?

**Well no, but that's how conversation flows. From one thing to the other. And I'm actually more interested in developing my campaign for old dogs who need a ride. You know, maybe people don't know about old dogs who get tired so it doesn't occur to them when they see me?**

I feel like this conversation has lost its direction. Though I have noticed you're struggling more to get up the driveway. I hate to call Dad to pick us up because the extra effort required to climb the hill is very likely why you're not losing even more muscle mass in your rear than I see right now. And I've noticed that your breathing is a bit labored lately - have you noticed it? So more cardiovascular effort might be a good idea.

**I don't know. Sometimes I don't feel so great when I walk up the driveway. Maybe more flat walks is the answer, and Dad can pick us up for the last stretch.**

Let me think about it. We want to do the right thing for you - keep you healthy, but not push you too hard. It's tricky! Maybe we should chat with the vet about it.

**Maybe we shouldn't chat with the vet about it. I'm about done with the vet. However, all this talk about walking has caused me to look out the window. And do you know what I see there? The new grass looks fresh and dewy. That makes for amazing scenting conditions.**

I don't doubt that. Would you like me to open the door so that you can go into the backyard?

**I've already sniffed around the backyard.**

Okay.

**Okay?**

What?

**There's much more to sniffing than wandering around my own backyard! All we have to do for a little extra sniffing excitement is to go out the front door, turn right, walk about twenty yards, and head down the driveway to the trailhead. From there, there are about four solid miles of sniffing, just for us! And anyway... you promised.**

I was sort of waiting for the rain to taper off.

**By the time the rain tapers off, it will be dark. Then I'll be stuck in the house because you never want to go out in the dark, even though it wouldn't bother me. Plus. You promised.**

How about if we go in about an hour when I've wrapped up my work?

**That would be great. I'm looking forward to it! Is this a promise?**

Yes it is, Raika. I promise.

**Okay.**

So why don't you go and lie down while you wait?

**I'm fine here. I'll just sit here and watch you until you're ready to go.**

That's unnerving. Every time I move my head, you perk up.

**That's because you usually move your head before you stand up, and you always stand up before we start our walk.**

I know, but I move my head when I'm not standing up, and when we're not about to go on our walk, too.

**I'm not sure I get your point.**

My point is that you can go and rest. I will let you know when it's time to go.

**Are you kidding? Anticipation is half the fun! I will stay here and watch you. You can ignore me if you like.**

Shall we just go right now?

**Well... if you insist. I'll meet you at the front door. Don't forget your raincoat. Revive that walking list, check the boxes, and let's get on with it.**

I will! With extra snacks for you. Raika, we need to do something about your appetite.

**Sure, extra snacks! Let's go before you start to waffle. You do that sometimes.**

Let's go. Tell you what. I'm going to try to see what you smell.

## Raika & Mom

**Mom, you're home!**

I came to walk you. I've been busy helping a friend, but I didn't want to miss another walk. I miss our walks, and I miss you, and I miss trying to see what you smell. I hope Lyra kept you good company.

**She did, plus Dad was here to keep me company as well.**

Okay, we'll go in a few minutes. I need to get something to eat first.

**How about a walking snack? Then we can leave right now. It's getting dark early again and I hate to miss out.**

Don't worry, I'll find something quick. But I need to eat.

**No walking snack? You need a fully sitting snack?**

It's hard to walk and eat at the same time. I have to hold your leash, your poop bags, and bring my phone to take pictures of you. Let me finish up a quick something and we'll be on our way.

**How much longer until we leave, approximately?**

Probably 10 or 15 minutes?

**Wow. That's a long time when you add in all the waiting I've been doing, especially since you still have the option of a walking snack.**

I'll get it down to five or ten minutes okay? Just a few bites.

**Okay. Should I wait here by you or by the door?**

You should wait wherever you'd like.

**Well, I'd like to wait on my bed, but I'm afraid if you see me there, you'll lose your sense of urgency, so I need to look at least somewhat uncomfortable. Or maybe you could eat sitting by my bed so you're uncomfortable; that might hurry you along a bit. How much time do we have left?**

I'm still looking in the fridge. The more you talk, the harder it is for me to think about what I'm trying to do.

**Are you trying to make this my fault?**

No, Raika. It's no one's fault. I'm just trying to eat so we can go on our walk.

**Then we're on the same page. I'll sit here next to your eating chair. Then we'll go for a walk, right?**

Yes. First a sandwich, and then we go for a walk.

**Perfect. I'm right here on the side closest to the door in case you forget why you're here.**

I see that.

> **Plus, do you see how I look at the door every once in a while?**

Hard to miss.

> **Excellent. We're seeing eye to eye. I'm settled in but ready to go at a moment's notice! And knowing how life is fragile - even short - we want to be careful about any unnecessary delay. As you know, at close to fifteen years of age, each day is a gift. So just say the word and I'll be ready.**

## Chapter 40:
### Dying is Not a Linear Process

## Mom & Raika

Raika, did you like your new walk yesterday? The one we drove to in the RV?

**I liked the place, but there sure were a lot of hills.**

I tried to give you plenty of breaks. Not enough?

**Mostly it just felt like a lot of up.**

Okay. Well, if you like that park, I will study the map and see if I can find a route that's a little bit flatter. Would that be better?

**Yes, I think that's a good idea. Plus, why the leash?**

It's a leash park. I kind of liked it; all of the other dogs were on leash, too.

**It was okay. You stopped when I wanted to sniff, so I can work with that.**

I don't like that we have to drive to get there, but it's nice to see a change of scenery. Plus, if we take the RV, you can really stretch out and we can make a full day adventure of it!

**That sounds amazing. We could visit the woods and open fields and beaches and explore! Let's just get rid of the hills.**

No worries, now we have a plan going forward. Let's turn the RV into a first class Raika-Mobile and visit new horizons with lots of flat areas. And we'll walk slowly - plenty of time for sniffing. Hey, can I ask you a question? I was curious if there was anything really amazing out there today? Something you might want to tell me about?

**Sure! So this park doesn't have any mountain lions in it, but it has a fox, and she has babies. They're getting bigger now and they're just starting to hunt on their own. That's why you can smell the fearful rabbits - they're afraid and trying to hide, but they need to come out and eat, too, so they zig zag back and forth before going back into hiding. Hunger drives them out, but the smell of fear is always with the rabbits. But the fox kits - they're still young and having a great time! No responsibilities for them; they're so small that they are mostly practicing their hunting. Their mom does the real work when they are hungry and need to eat.**

Thank you, Raika. So the fox babies play, the momma fox hunts, and the rabbits are afraid?

**Yeah, pretty much.**

Those poor rabbits. Always afraid of death.

**No, Mom, the rabbits are not afraid of death - they are afraid of dying. For a rabbit, the end is almost always violent and scary. That's what drives their fear, not the end of life.**

## Mom & Raika

You know, Raika, I had a thought.

**What's that?**

I was thinking that maybe when I'm walking through the house - for example, in the kitchen or the bedroom - I was thinking that maybe you could find a place to stand other than the doorway or the middle of the room.

**But then how would you notice me?**

I'm quite confident that I would notice you even if you were not in the center of the room. Maybe closer to the wall?

**You want me to be a wallflower?**

Well, no. That sort of implies that no one would see you. I am absolutely certain that we would see you. I'm just thinking that when you stand in the doorway, and then you don't move no matter how many times I go back and forth... I'm just thinking that might be inconvenient for you?

**Nope.**

Oh. Well, we're worried you'll get hurt. You know, someone might trip over you because you have a tendency to be exactly where everyone is walking?

**Honestly, I don't think you need to worry. What I have observed is that the human falls over but I'm fine.**

So it's the falling over part. I was wondering if we could do something about that. For example, when you see someone stumbling over you, you could take that as your cue to head for the wall. Or your dog bed.

**I need to think about this a bit. When one considers that I might only be on this earth for a few more days or weeks, it seems that everyone would want me right in the middle of the action. I mean, don't misunderstand me. I totally understand. But I also have to consider the feelings of the rest of the family.**

On this occasion, I think the entire family is in alignment. Alternatively, you could move when somebody approaches. Maybe just pay a little more attention?

**Well, that's kind of hard because I don't actually hear you guys anymore. When did everyone start speaking so softly?**

I'm not getting anywhere.

**That's not true at all! I just don't think your idea is a very good one, being as there's only days or weeks left...**

That's fine. And don't forget months or years, Raika. Could be years.

**Exactly! How fortunate that would be!**

Good thing I love you so much, because many more years of Raika also means many more years of sleep deprivation.

**In what sense?**

You had another rough night last night. Dad found you. First you were walking in random circles, and then you were trying to go through a closed closet door. It was really upsetting. He brought you back several times, but you just didn't want to settle.

**I may have been patrolling the hallway for bad guys; that's a big part of a dog's job, you know.**

Well, unless the bad guy is hiding in the closet, I'm not sure it makes much sense to try and walk through a closed door. It's disconcerting when you do that. We are all much happier when you sleep through the night and stay on your bed.

**There is nothing to worry about - and most definitely no reason to call the vet! Not like it's a regular occurrence.**

But that's the thing. It's becoming a regular occurrence. I'd say it's about two times a week now; I'd call that regular. Maybe tonight you'll sleep extra well.

**I feel fine. Although I wonder if a high-quality bedtime snack might help? Or even a short walk right before it's time to sleep? To make sure I'm tired?**

You think snacks and walks fix everything. Which would be fine, except lately you don't even eat those snacks that you keep asking for. You've lost five pounds. I do miss those days when an extra snack seemed to fix anything. Old lady dog begging fell in the category of cute-old rather than weird-old. Although I guess both are better than sick-old.

**I'm definitely cute-old! Someday I'll get sick-old, but we're not talking about that right now. So stop worrying about tomorrow, and let's get on with today. Specifically, a sniffing walk.**

Your nighttime behavior is fully in the territory of weird-old.

**I'd suggest you repress that for now and admire how cute I am.**

Aren't you the one who is always saying the end could be any day, hour, or minute?

**Well yeah, but only when it's self-serving. If you're using that logic to bring out the vet, then I'd like to nip that train of thought in the bud. I'm fine. Let's not be using my manipulative tactics against me. Though I had another thought.**

What's that?

**Maybe I'm practicing being a ghost. You know, so after I die I can wander the halls and spook you - just a little.**

I'm going to pretend you didn't say that and go back to repression.

## Raika & Mom

**Mom?**

Yes, Raika?

**I've thought about your question: when will it be time for me to die? And I have an answer.**

I wish you would consider a more gradual introduction to conversations like that; we had that talk some time ago!

**I'm open to suggestions, but I don't know of any suitable opening lines. I just know it took me awhile to find my answer. I'm sorry if I upset you.**

So I'm going to take a deep breath, and then I want to hear what you decided.

**When I don't want to walk or swim or shred papers or sit by your side while you pet my head, then you'll know I have lost my interest in being here.**

How about if you need me constantly to feel good, but I can't always do those things for you, and your pills alone aren't working? Sometimes I have to leave the house, and I need to sleep at night. I cannot always take you out for a walk or a swim or pet your head, even though I can see how much those things make you feel better.

**Why couldn't you be there for me when I need you?**

Because sometimes I have other things in life that need to get done, too.

**Things that are more important than me?**

No, not more important than you. That's the thing, Raika. There are so many things that need doing. Humans try to do them all – and that can be hard. For example, sometimes I have to leave you here alone, even though I know you don't like to be alone anymore. And other days I really have to get some work done, even though I'd love to take you for a walk.

**Well then, do what you can. Your best. That's fine, too.**

That sounds simple enough. What if you don't want to walk for just for one day, or maybe even one week? Is one missed swim enough, or do you have to stop showing any interest in the activity at all? And what if I can keep the pain away but I just can't keep up with your other needs? And what about your eating, Raika? How much weight are you going to lose? How many meals can you miss before we get serious about figuring out an alternative? And then the biggest one, your behavior - it's erratic! One day you're doing great, and the next day I'm really scared for you.

**Dying is not a linear process.**

Raika, I'm worried about my ability to handle the end of your life. I'm afraid I'll get it wrong. Maybe I'll let you stay too long when · you want to go, or panic and let you go before it's really your time. Could I have managed another walk or swim? Maybe I could have found some other small change to make you feel better if you're having a bad day? Each morning I wake up and I ask myself, are you eating today? Are you stiff from too much exercise, or is the pain from your arthritis taking over? Will you sleep peacefully that night, or will you wander around, running into the walls or walking in circles? Have you lost more weight? You see, Raika? It's not black and white. It's all shades of gray.

**It doesn't matter if you let me go too soon - I'm not afraid of death.**

How can you say that? I cannot risk letting you go even one day too soon! You deserve to be here as long as possible!

**No, Mom, that's not true. You will keep me here for you - and that's okay. I love you so much, and I love life so much! But the truth is, life is hard. I have to think about everything - eating, walking, even breathing! I have lived an amazing life, and I have lived with you. But when the end comes, keeping me here will be for you and not for me.**

Raika, I cannot listen to this. You are wrong. You deserve to be here and take every last ounce from your life. That's not about me. And what I heard was that if you don't want to walk and you can't swim, or if I can't manage to keep you comfortable with all of my best efforts, then we need to talk about that.

**Yes, that's when we need to talk. But Mom, I'm not wrong. My living is about you - when you decide to let me go, it will be about me.**

I need to think. You know, we've been very lucky so far. You're almost fifteen years old, and besides random problems like arthritis and tummy troubles and the tendency to get tired easily, you have no real health problems. Well, except for your nighttime thing - that worries me. But so far it's only at night and we have found a way to manage that for now. For your age, that's kind of amazing. I love you, Raika. I really cannot imagine what life will look like when you're gone, but for now, I'm happy with how incredibly well you're doing.

**I love you too, Mom. I love you so much!**

# Chapter 41:
## Proactively Addressing Senseless Human Waste

### Raika & Mom

**What's up with the leash?**

You are in scavenging mode today. That makes you hard to supervise, so you're back on leash even when it's not required.

**Scavenging mode? Negative, negative, negative! I am proactively addressing senseless human waste! Half a burger here, a partial carcass there...**

Is that what you were eating? A carcass? I can't believe you're doing that again. That's just disgusting.

**Don't knock it till you try it. Plenty of beneficial enzymes in a half-chewed carcass.**

With thinking like that, a leash it is!

**It makes you look bad, you know. Did you hear that man offer me some water?**

The leash stays on.

**I think I will start limping. People will think you're dragging me! And I will do nothing to dissuade them of that notion until you remove the leash.**

You're not winning.

**Could be my last day of life, you know. My very last walk. Dragged down the street. On a leash. Oh! And Mom? While we're chatting... did you notice this tree here? It's going to die. The beetles have moved in and they're under the bark; you can smell it right here near the base. Now that the tree is weakening, there are gaps underneath where the roots are dying. That's where the pregnant**

**mouse will have her family. She must have moved in yesterday, because I don't remember smelling her here earlier; usually she's hanging out near that other tree about fifteen feet away - see it?**

I do see that tree, but I didn't know that mice lived under the roots. And no, I didn't know that the tree here had beetles, or that it will die soon. But I know now and I'll watch for it.

**Mom, I wish you could smell. I want to be able to share more with you.**

I wish I could, too, but I can't, so I'm counting on you to be my guide. I'll pay close attention so I can learn as much as possible.

**Sounds good. Better than nothing, right? Now if I were off leash, I could get to some of those further spaces - see over there where that ditch is? I bet I could tell you some amazing stories about what is happening over there.**

Good thing I have so much to learn; we can keep my learning right here in this section you can reach - on leash.

## Mom & Raika

I think you are really going to enjoy your breakfast, Raika. I made you a combination of tripe and leftover beef fat from last night.

**It's very cute how you made two eyes out of the peanut butter balls and put them at the top.**

I'm glad you appreciate my creativity. Now eat up!

**First of all, I want you to know that I do appreciate the effort you put into my breakfast this morning. Very creative! Unfortunately, I am fasting at this time.**

Fasting? What are you talking about?

**I've heard that fasting is a very good thing to do on**

occasion. **It gives your stomach a chance to rest. So, today I am fasting. Or at least, right now I am.**

Raika, you have never fasted for your health in your life. There's no reason to start now.

**That's because I was young and silly and thought the whole world revolves around food. I am wiser now, and I have decided to take up the occasional fast.**

Please eat your breakfast.

**I'm not going to eat my breakfast.**

You're being silly. Eat your breakfast.

**I'm not hungry. I'm not going to eat this morning.**

You just told me you were fasting. Now you say you're not hungry. Which is it?

**I knew this would happen. Whenever I say I'm not hungry, you start freaking out like I'll be dead in four hours. So I thought I would tell you I was fasting instead. But the truth is, I'm just not hungry right now.**

But you have to be hungry.

**But I don't.**

We can negotiate this. Eat the little peanut butter balls. I can serve the rest as a snack later on today.

**No thank you.**

The peanut butter balls are not optional.

**Yes, they are. And I'm not eating them.**

Raika, I'm serious. If you don't eat the peanut butter balls, I'm going to have to dissect them, pull out the middle part, and stuff it down your throat.

**That does not sound at all appealing, but you've done it before under similar circumstances, so I suppose I'm resigned to it.**

Raika, please eat the peanut butter balls. Or maybe cream cheese would be better? Would you like me to find some cream cheese and make you some cream cheese balls?

**Look. I know what's going on here. You're afraid that if I miss a meal, I'll be dead tomorrow. The fact is, I have missed many meals over the course of this past year and I'm not dead yet.**

I get that. But you have to agree that once you are dead, you won't eat anything. I'm worried that you're practicing.

**That might be the first joke you've made about my death. Which seems like a good start! Even if it was at my expense.**

Glad you're pleased. Now eat.

**I'll keep my eyes out for trash on my walk. That usually perks up my appetite.**

## Mom

She's down seven pounds. She can't afford to lose seven pounds. She's also had soft stools for a few days – and I'm pretty sure there was a trace of blood today.

Then her walk today took almost two hours. I'm not complaining about the time because I'm happy to be out there with her, but that's almost twice as long it usually takes us to cover the same ground. Maybe it's the coming heat of summer slowing her down? I know I always start out a little impatient, but then I adapt and try to take in the world from her point of view. And that is a truly amazing point of view, isn't it? How she sees the world - what a miracle that is. Today, I stood there with her thinking all of those thoughts, admiring who she is.

And then she vomited. A lot.

So we kept going - slowly. But then I wondered if that was the right decision. She was lethargic. Should I have taken her home instead? Should I shorten our future walks, or is that going to cause more problems than it solves?

I know she's not a fan of going to the vet, but I had to do something, so I emailed the vet. I'm not panicking, honest. The last time this happened, a few days of antibiotics cleared it right up. So I'm hopeful that she snagged one too many rotten bits of something off the trail and her tummy is a little out of whack. Maybe it means nothing. Maybe it means everything.

That little joke that she admired after she refused to eat? I'm glad she found that funny because it just about ripped my heart out.

I already promised that I would never leave her alone at the vet clinic. Can I keep that promise? What if she only needs IV fluids? Would that be okay - just one night at the clinic - or is that still too scary? How would I ever forgive myself if she died there, alone and afraid, without me by her side?

The alternative is to keep her at home no matter what. Is that what I should do? Even if she needs specialized care? Shall I just ask for medication to keep her comfortable and at home?

I think about it from every angle, running in circles, until I exhaust myself.

I have set a goal for myself. I am working to admire and appreciate every single day while accepting it for what it is - a step towards the end. I have been given the gift of an old dog, and while our future cannot be known, I can be grateful for what I do know. I've already been given quite a lot. Appreciation with awareness. I believe she would approve.

Raika is an extraordinary gift indeed. I won't waste it.

Part Two

# Summer 2019

### Chapter 42:
### The Cycle of Life

Raika & Mom

**You will be pleased to know that I ate my breakfast. And the addition of jelly to my peanut butter balls was sheer brilliance on your part! You know I have a sweet tooth.**

You did! You ate your breakfast today - and your peanut butter balls!

**Are you feeling any better from your worrying about me?**

Absolutely!

**Do you find it at all ironic that I am asking if you're feeling better when I'm the one who misses meals? You know, if you get that worked up over a missed meal, what's your plan for when I really am struggling? Are you going to have any worry left for those times?**

I think worry is one of those things that just multiplies; it doesn't seem to be available in limited quantities, although I wish it were.

**Are you getting ready for the end with all of your worry?**

This is what people do, Raika. We alternate between worry and panic and guilt, and all of that eats at our heart and emotions until we exhaust ourselves. And then we are left with an emptiness and a very deep sadness.

**Mom, it has to be that way. You're making room for my molecules. If it didn't hurt enough to leave a hole inside of you, then where would they fit?**

I hadn't thought of that. Is the pain needed to make the hole?

**It's like when babies come into this world. The pain of labor begins well in advance. That pain is required to open up a hole in the body and is at its worst when the baby is actually born, but then we love and appreciate them more than we ever thought possible.**

But you're not being born. You're going to leave me.

**The hole in your heart is opening up now, while we are still together, so my molecules will fit. You're preparing. This is why death in the young or when it is unexpected is so hard; there's no time to make room for the molecules. Mom, life and death all fit together. The pain, the molecules, and the appreciation for all we've had and for what is still to come - it's a cycle that needs to happen. When I die, it will not be a tragedy. It will mean my time has come after a full cycle of life! The tragedy is for those who are left behind, that you cannot find acceptance and comfort in the cycle of life.**

You're right, Raika. That is the tragedy.

## Raika & Mom

**I would like to tell a story. Would you like to hear it?**

Sure. What's your story about?

**The squirrel on the driveway!**

The one we saw yesterday?

**Yes, that one!**

Well, I'm happy to hear the story, but I was there the entire time.

**You might've missed a few things. You know, the little details that make a story come to life?**

Yes, I might have. Go ahead and tell me the story.

**Well, I was trotting down the driveway, minding my own business, when all of a sudden, straight out from the vegetable garden, a squirrel leaped right onto the driveway practically in front of me!**

Yes! That is exactly what I saw happen!

**So I instantly put on the afterburners and chased that squirrel! My jaws were snapping three inches from its neck!**

I thought I saw you trot rather sedately in his general direction... Sorry. Go on. I'm listening.

**Anyway, at the last moment, his little life flashed before my eyes. So instead of killing him, I held him to the ground with one paw and told him never to enter the vegetable garden again! Then I let them go, at which point he ran up the tree.**

It happened just like that?

**Pretty close. One of the best parts of storytelling is the embellishment part!**

So we're thinking this is a fiction story?

**Not at all! This is nonfiction. I am describing it exactly as it happened in my head. And since you are not in my head, you missed the details. I got the beginning and the end right, with just a few tweaks to the middle.**

Yes, Raika, you're absolutely right. It happened just like that, and I'm quite sure that squirrel learned his lesson and will never come back.

**Good thing I'm here!**

I say that every day. Good thing you're here, because I don't know what I'll do when you're not.

# Chapter 43:
## 150 Pounds of Expensive Meat

## Mom & Raika

Good morning, and happy 15th birthday to you, Raika!

**Thank you! What's on the agenda?**

You didn't ask for very much this year, but of course we'll go for our walk. Would you like a flat walk nearby, or to go in the car to a new place with a flat trail?

**A flat walk, but let's take the Raika-Mobile and head out while it's cool.**

Absolutely, we will do that. And what would you like for dinner?

**How about duck with pretzels sprinkled on top and some cherry jam?**

I'll make you that. Is there anything else you want?

**There's just not much left to ask for, is there? Can you do something about my hearing? It's becoming an embarrassment. I can't hear a damned thing anymore.**

Unfortunately, that comes with age. There's nothing I can do about that.

**Well, that's unfortunate. I am missing my good ears. Now that I think about it, I'm missing my good balance, too - and my good lungs. I stumble more when I get up, and my lungs, they're just not what they used to be. Do you remember when I could bike for miles and miles and barely get winded? Now I struggle just to get up the driveway.**

We'll take as many breaks as you need on our walks. Getting old is hard, Raika.

**Yes, it is.**

If you're uncomfortable, we can go back to the vet and see which pain medications can be adjusted. I've noticed how you're struggling more lately. And Raika?

**Yes?**

I'm sorry we're having this conversation on your birthday.

**It's okay. Kind of a weird conversation today, but you know? It really is okay. Let's go in the Raika-Mobile, have an awesome walk, and then you can whip up my birthday dinner, which I may or may not actually eat.**

Perfect. Oh, I almost forgot! The pool - it's warm enough to start swimming. Are you ready to head back to the pool?

**My birthday just got perfect! Thank you so much! Today I will swim and see if I can get back some of the muscle mass I've lost. When will we start?**

Hmm. Now?

**Great minds think alike. I'm ready and waiting.**

So, Raika. Before we swim, can we talk about the sinking toy? I truly hate to have this conversation on your birthday, but we need to discuss it.

**The one that went missing at the end of the swim season last year? Does this mean you found it? Where was it? I certainly hope you didn't find it in the trash like last time. I can only imagine how narrowly we escaped disaster. What if I hadn't been with you in the garage on that fateful day so long ago?**

No, it was not in the trash. It was in the garage, though, in the very back where the books are.

**It's so strange about that toy. Considering I go pretty**

much everywhere, it is quite the coincidence that it keeps
finding itself in places that I never go.

Indeed. It's like a cat; that toy has nine lives and then some. I was
pretty sure it was a goner many times, and yet there it is again.
Regardless, it's back now and you can use it - but only on the steps.

**Oh, for sure! This is my lucky toy! On another note, I'd
like to see that expression changed. It paints cats in much
too favorable of a light. Anyway, now that we've found my
sinking toy again, I'm heading out to start the season with
a spectacular dive smack dab in the middle of the pool!**

I think you didn't hear me. You can only use it on the steps.

**I can't dive on the steps - they're not even under two feet
of water! I thought you meant I was supposed to start my
jumps from the steps.**

I was thinking you could stand on the top step and just reach out and
grab it from the second step.

**How is that diving? That's not diving.**

Your head will go fully underwater with this plan - that is diving!

**So. No more sinking toy. What's next? No more floating
toy? Then no more swimming? Are the walks on the
chopping block, too? Soon we'll be sitting in the house
just looking at each other, waiting for dinner - for you,
that is, since my appetite is spotty. Is that what you want?**

Raika, keeping you happy means the world to me. You can swim
and walk as long as you want. But the diving and swimming in the
deep end has to stop now. I'm sorry. Before we found the diving toy
at the end of last year, you were pretty happy with your floaty toys
and playing in the shallow end. You'd almost forgotten about the
diving toy.

**Loss of hope is not a memory problem. It's resignation.**

Look on the bright side - this is your favorite time of year! Lots of opportunity for walks and swims and day trips in the Raika-Mobile!

**It would mean a lot to you if I stayed in the shallow end?**

Yes, Raika. It would mean a lot to me if you would stay in the shallow end.

**I'm a pretty good diver, as we both know.**

It's not that. It's just that you could get turned upside down in the water and I'd have to pull you out. Do you remember when that happened last year? It was upsetting to both of us, and that was a full year ago. What if Brito sees me dragging you out of the pool?

**Good point. I'd never hear the end of it.**

Yeah, that's what I was thinking. Better to keep your dignity intact.

**Still good to have my toy back, though. That's good anyway.**

Nine lives.

## Mom & Raika

Good morning, Raika. Are you hungry?

**Meh. Not so much. What's on the menu?**

Something good! Ground beef.

**Raw or cooked?**

Mostly pink with a little brown around the edges. Nice and warm, but not overcooked.

**One big chunk or broken up?**

Broken up.

**Let me see it.**

What do you think?

**Are you going to feed it to me, or put it in my bowl?**

I can feed it to you.

**I'll eat a few bites.**

Great! Plus, this little piece here.

**That's a pill pocket. I know what that is, and I don't want it.**

How about we alternate? A piece of ground beef, and then a pill pocket?

**Maybe three pieces of ground beef, and then a pill pocket.**

Okay. And then I'll follow it up really quickly with another piece of ground beef. You'll barely notice.

**Oh, I'll notice all right. I can recognize a pill pocket a mile away. I mean, I've eaten something like a thousand of them now. Plus, I don't actually want the ground beef.**

Just pretend it's delicious ground beef and eat it quickly.

**Why don't we just skip breakfast instead?**

Because some pills are twice a day. I need a bit of food in you for that.

**Fine, a couple of bites.**

Let's just get through this meal and on with the rest of the day.

**Mom, am I cute-old or worry-old?**

Mornings are hard with the breakfast thing. Then you're worry-old. And that nighttime stuff is 100% weird-old. But still, I'd say you have lots of cute-old, with a healthy dash of weird-old and worry-old thrown in to keep me on my toes. And when you stop walking on your walks and Dad has to come and get us? When you seem to be struggling? That is 100% worry-old. The worry-old stage is very hard on humans, Raika, though better than the sick-old stage.

**I don't mean to make you worry, but I'm not hungry.**

I know, and as a matter of fact, I went shopping today and most of it is for you.

**Seriously? What did you buy me?**

Remember how you gobbled up that ground lamb a few weeks ago? I found it on sale today, so I stocked up and bought forty pounds!

**Lamb? Yeah. The lamb was pretty good back then.**

Wait, what do you mean by "back then"? Is lamb not good now?

**I'm not feeling lamb right now. What else did you buy?**

Do you remember how much you liked goat when you were a puppy? That was your favorite meal! And I found goat! Better yet, it's all cut up into nice little chunks, ready for you to eat.

**Goat? That might be okay. Well. I don't know. I don't think I'm feeling goat right now.**

You don't want the goat? I can show it to you and you can decide?

**I don't know. Maybe I'll want it tomorrow. For now, you can give it to Lyra and Brito. What else did you buy?**

Just a few other random things to try. Oh! How about duck? Do you want duck? I bought that, too, but you eat so much duck I thought maybe you were just tired of it.

**Duck? How are you going to prepare it?**

How about if I pull all the meat off the bones and fry the chunks? Then I can give it to you when it's still warm and the house smells like fried meat.

**What about a sauce? Maybe some cherries? Do we have cherries?**

Actually, Raika, we do. We have some in the freezer. Let me see what I can do.

**That's super! It will look just like a nice Thanksgiving meal!**

Yes, it will. So are you going to eat it after I make it?

**I'm not sure yet. Maybe. But I might change my mind.**

Raika, when you won't eat, you're worry-old.

**Mom, I just have a bad tummy and I'm not too hungry. I know you're worried and feeling sorry for me, but you know what? I'm not. I don't feel sorry for me at all. I take each moment and each day as it comes. I'm living right now, not in the past where I've been, or in the future where I'm going to be.**

Well, if I'm not supposed to worry, what should I do?

**If I were you, I'd be kind of mad. You've got 150 pounds of expensive meat, and I have no particular plans to eat it.**

## Mom & Raika

What would you like for your walking snack today?

**Anything will be fine.**

I knock myself out trying to find you tasty food for your meals, and nothing appeals to you. Yet we take a walk, and you're thrilled if I hand you a Cheerio.

**Cheerios are tasty when you eat them meandering along in the warm sunshine while admiring the sniffing spots. Really, almost everything is tasty at such a momentous time!**

Cheerios are not tasty when you eat them in our comfy house?

**It's not the same at all! You know how you walk by a bowl of nuts and grab a handful? And then you just put them in your mouth without thinking? That's what happens when we're out on a walk. When you hand me something, I eat it without thinking about it one way or the other - just in the mouth and down the hatch it goes!**

Humans call that mindless eating.

**Dogs are the masters of mindless eating! If you doubt this, open up a bag of kibble in front of a Labrador. You don't really think he's hungry as he eats the last five pounds, do you? More like, "Get while the gettin's good!" and then it becomes a habit.**

I see. So if I bring your breakfast along on our walk and I give it to you somewhere outside, will you eat it?

**Well no, because now we have the context problem. You have to hand it to me from your pocket, not from a bowl.**

I hand you food in the house. Sometimes you eat it, and sometimes you don't.

**That's because in the house we have a different context problem - sometimes you hand me food that has pills in it. While my memory is not what it used to be, I do know to be suspicious when you hand me something in the kitchen.**

Well, clever you.

**Clever me.**

Is it warm enough that we should swim before we head out?

**Absolutely! A quick splash in the pool might be just the thing.**

Speaking of the pool, I've noticed that pool time is a little different this year.

**In what sense?**

Well, I've noticed that mostly you just trot around the pool, but don't jump in so much. And when you're in the pool, you tend to head to the steps pretty quickly. Jumping and diving have always been your favorite parts, so it worries me that some days you only go in once or twice.

**Somehow my "jumping in" muscles have lost their jump.**

That can happen for sure, especially at the beginning of the season. So maybe you could hop in by the steps and just paddle around a bit to cool off?

**This might come as a surprise to you, but I don't actually care about swimming. I care about leaping in as high and as far as I can go, or about going to the very bottom to get a toy. But then I return to the steps to start over again. I don't really swim just to swim.**

Now that you mention it, that's true. The only time you swim in circles is when you don't want to get out.

**The last time I tried to swim for a toy, I had to turn back after ten feet. It's like my lungs just aren't working very hard anymore.**

I've noticed that on your walks, as well. Lots of panting and effort, even when we're not doing a whole lot. Do you think it's the heat? Some days I really wonder if we should stop going out altogether. Maybe this is age, Raika. Maybe getting old means not being able to breathe properly when you go for walks or long swims.

**Not swimming or walking is simply not optional. Remember our quality of life discussions? I need to go for walks and swims. But wow - some days it really is hard.**

I'm going to have a chat with the vet. Don't worry, she's not going to come out right away, but I'd like to get an expert opinion. It's probably nothing more than getting a little older.

**Probably. Feel like I have fewer and fewer options open to me these days.**

Chapter 44:
The Substitute Vet

## Mom & Raika

The substitute vet says all of your internal organs are perfect. Great lungs, great heart, great everything. No signs of tumors, either. They x-rayed everything, and you are the picture of internal health. But you're supposed to take it easy for a few weeks until you're a little more stable on your feet again.

**What does that mean?**

No walks. No swims.

**That's outrageous! I want my regular vet back!**

She's out of town for a few days, so we took the one we could get. I called a few days ago when I saw you struggling to breathe again - seems a little exertion shouldn't be causing you that much trouble.

**I have no idea how this one even got through vet school. She should have failed out the first semester. No walks and no swims - what a dummy.**

Well I'm not convinced either, so don't kill me in my sleep.

**You're safe. Frankly, I'm not sure I could jump on the bed.**

FYI, you didn't do me any favors when I said it's been hard to get you to eat and then you ate every damned thing she offered you.

**You put pills in the middle of cookies. Also, the chicken jerky she had was pretty good. You should buy that.**

And you knew perfectly well what I wanted when I told you to lay down. I hope she doesn't know I'm a dog trainer.

**Why not bribe me with one of those chicken jerky**

**cookies?**

I should just stop taking you to the vet.

**No argument from me.**

I didn't mean that; I'm still taking you to the vet.

**Use the good vet! Send her a letter of complaint about this substitute. Everyone knows how hard it is to get fitness back once you stop exercising.**

Would you like your breakfast now? Got some good stuff here.

**No thanks. Not hungry.**

## Raika & Mom

**Mom, can you tell me a bedtime story?**

Sure. Let me think of a topic.

**Something I can relate to, please.**

Relate to? I usually tell you stories about your life! That should be very relatable. But there are guests here, so we need to be a little quiet.

**You don't need to be quiet. I can't hear you anyway. You can just talk to me in your head.**

You can't hear me at all?

**No, I don't think so. I barely hear anything that's not in my head. When I do hear something, I jump up and... nothing. There's nothing there! Nothing happening.**

Probably dreams.

**When I was young, I could tell the difference.**

You're older now.

**I guess. I can't see much either.**

That's okay. There's not much you need to see.

**I'm not sure I could see the toy even if you did throw it in the pool. So even if I manage to get in and try to swim to it, it feels a bit like a lost cause.**

We can work out a different game for you. I'll think about that.

**Okay. Also my sniffer isn't working quite right, either. It takes me forever to find the treats you drop on the floor.**

But your sense of taste is fully intact - that's a big plus.

**That is true. No sneaking second-rate food past me! I'll have the best or nothing at all!**

Exactly. And you look amazing. Barely any white on your face at all. Not a day over ten.

**I wanted a bedtime story, but I'm not sure I want to hear about my younger days when everything worked well.**

You were an amazing young dog, and you're an amazing older dog, too - running the show while we follow you around and clean up after your misbehavior. Speaking of which, you need to stop taking the plastic bottles off the table before they are empty. You're making a mess with that. We need to find something less messy for you to do.

**I like how they smash and crinkle in my mouth. Maybe just ask people to empty them faster?**

Maybe that's perfect. Do you still want a story?

**Soon, but not today. Somehow, a story featuring a blind, deaf, and smelless Belgian who retired from world-class competition doesn't seem very action packed. More of a comedy about a washed-up has-been. And when I'm featured in a comedy, we are teetering on a tragedy.**

There's no tragedy. But if you decide you want a story with a blind, deaf, and smelless Belgian, I'll think one up. You were amazing the day you were born. You were amazing in your competition career. And you're amazing right now, too.

**Thanks, Mom. Going to sleep now.**

Good night, Raika.

**Good night, Mom.**

# Chapter 45:
## Raika's Book

### Raika & Mom

**A book? You're talking to your friends about writing a book about me?! What a fantastic idea, Mom!**

I'm glad you like the idea! I'm excited about sharing your story with anyone who wants to read it.

**Well, you certainly couldn't find a better subject for a book than me! Witty, good-looking, interesting - what more could a reader want in their heroine? Plus, I have stories to tell. There are things that I know as a result of my maturity and the wisdom that comes with age. A book! What a great way to share my story! I'll admit, however, that I'm a little surprised you're discussing the end of my story already. I mean, my days may be numbered, but I'm not dead yet. I say we start working on it now and the end will come when it comes.**

That works for me.

**Let's start by deciding which stories will go in and which ones won't. For example, the one where I got into a fight with that dog and you landed in the ditch with the guy on top of you? We don't need that one. Also, we should leave out the stories about me peeing in the house since we can all agree that it's not my fault. Skip the ones where I got scared of loud noises, or where my hearing wasn't too good - or worse, non-existent. Oh, and the ones where Lyra needs to keep me company because I get scared when you're not home. Those are not the kinds of stories I want to publicize.**

Those are important stories, Raika. We can't change our life's story into something it's not.

**When writing a book, the door is wide open for creative license. And anyway, when I do leave this earth, I want to leave people with a good impression of me. No one wants to admit they peed on their own dog bed.**

I'm sorry, Raika. Those stories happened, and they need to be included in the book.

**This is going to be a lot less fun if you insist on sticking to reality.**

Are you still game to have your stories published?

**I suppose so. By the time you publish it, I'll be dead, so I guess it won't matter.**

Lord, Raika, what makes you say things like that? Let's go back to your earlier statement: you're not dead yet!

**And looking pretty good, if I do say so myself.**

## Mom & Raika

Raika, I need to tell you something sad.

**What's that?**

Your sister Emmy? She died a few days ago. She had an amazing life, but her time came.

**She was the pink puppy, right? Yes, that is sad. Her mom loved her a lot, I think.**

Yes, she did. Her mom is heartbroken. Can you do anything to help with the molecule transfer?

**I don't think so. That comes later. Emmy has to work that out for herself.**

Hopefully she put a few aside for her mom.

**I bet she did... Mom, do you know what will happen to Emmy's toys?**

Her toys?

**Yeah. Maybe they could be sent over here?**

Raika, I don't think this is the right time to be asking about that.

**Yeah, you're probably right. Her mom is sad. Just like you'll be sad when my time comes. You won't be thinking about toys.**

Raika, this thing with your breathing... I feel like the vet may have missed something important, but don't worry - we'll see your regular vet next week and sort it out.

**I think I have my best days after we go places. We should do that more often. Take a trip in the Raika-Mobile.**

We should.

**I do kinda wonder what happened to Emmy's toys though.**

Might be best to keep that thought to yourself.

## Mom

Hon, come home right away. Raika passed out. I'm at the emergency vet, and the other dogs are still in the pool area. I need you to bring them in, give them dinner, and get them settled. Raika's in an oxygen tank now. As soon as I see the vet, I'll let you know what's happening. I'm scared. I'm not ready to lose her.

## Mom & Raika

Hi Raika,

I know I promised you I wouldn't leave you at the vet, but I didn't have a choice. You couldn't breathe, and I could see the panic in your face. Something is going wrong inside of you. You were right about the substitute vet; she missed something important. We don't know what it is yet, but passing out after trotting around the pool is far from normal - you're suffocating. So I either had to leave you and let them try to find the problem, or let you go forever. I can't do that yet, so I left you just this once. I know you don't see me, but I am with you every second until you're home again.

Raika, I keep seeing your face when you fell - your mouth open and your eyes wide with fear. I couldn't let you go, and I couldn't leave you. I hope you understand why I reneged on my promise. I'll still provide all of your follow-up care myself right here at home, and I promise you - I remember all of our conversations. But right now? It's not your time yet, I'm sure of it. We just need to find the problem so that we can make an informed choice about what to do next.

The vet asked me some really hard questions, Raika. They're putting you under anesthesia, and sometimes that can be dangerous, even with a team of people there watching over you just as carefully as I do. They asked me what I wanted to do if you stopped breathing, or if they found a mass in your throat. They asked me about things that I have thought about a lot but that I'm not ready to make real with the words that could end your life.

I'm doing my best, Raika, but I know I don't always make good decisions when I'm scared - and right now I'm scared. I tried to remember all of our conversations, all of the things we talked about. I told the vet about swimming and walking and what it means for you to have a good life. I think she understood.

You know what I forgot to tell her? I forgot to tell her that you are the most important dog in the world, and that because of that she has to do her absolute best job. I wish I had told her that.

Raika? Be good with the vets, stay calm, and I'll bring you home as soon as they tell me to come and get you.

Love, Mom

**Hi, Mom!**

**First of all, I want to tell you it's not that bad here.** I told the main vet that I am a Very Important Dog, and I think she may have understood because she's spending a lot of time watching me. Several of her vet friends have stopped by to see me, too. I was careful not to say the MOST important dog, just in case she has dogs of her own; under the circumstances, I figured I should stay on her good side.

Anyway, like I said, it's not too bad. A little bit of poking and prodding, but nothing terrible. Of course they haven't served any meals yet, so I reserve judgment on the place until that happens. In the meantime, I have a quiet place to rest while they work out the details and create a plan for the rest of my day.

I don't know if anyone has called you yet, but they're hoping to avoid surgery with another test. Depending on the results, it's possible that I can come home and get back to my normal life with a new medication for you to hide in various foods - which I will promptly refuse to eat, of course.

I'd like to remind you about our quality-of-life discussions. If you haven't been very clear already, you could set those as a baseline before I go into surgery.

I hope she calls you soon so you can stop worrying so much. Personally, I have a good feeling about this. I'm mostly healthy and strong and beautiful - though that last part might not be too relevant right now. Maybe most importantly, I want to end my life with dignity; I want to be able to take something from each day with joy, and with you by my side. When I have nothing more to take, and nothing more to give, then you need to find the strength to let me go. But I don't think today is that day, so keep your spirits up. I plan to be home soon.

**With love, Raika**

# Part Three

# Fall 2019

### Chapter 46:
### Raika's Condition!

## Mom & Raika

Good morning, Raika. You have no idea how glad I am to have you back home.

**Good morning, Mom! You have no idea how glad I am to be back home!**

You had a restful night's sleep. That's good.

**I did. Shall we go for an early morning walk before it gets hot? The vet said I'm not supposed to get too hot with My Condition.**

Actually, what the vet said is that you need to rest until we stabilize your medication.

**No walk? Didn't you hear what the vet said about My Condition? It's very serious! I could drop dead at any moment.**

Didn't you hear what she said about resting for a while?

**Maybe in passing.**

So, about these pills. What do you think about cream cheese?

**No, thank you.**

Liverwurst?

**No, thank you.**

Sausage?

**No, thank you.**

Raika! Stop being difficult.

**My Condition!**

Okay - these are chicken with mango bits. Does that sound good?

**Yeah, that sounds okay. I'll take those.**

I can't believe we have to do these pills three times a day.

**You know, the tried-and-true method is to take me for a walk and slip those pills in when I'm not thinking about it. I won't even notice them going down.**

No walks for a week.

**Figured it was worth a try.**

Raika & Mom

**I feel good! Air goes in and out like it's nothing! Amazing what modern medicine can do. What a fine day for a walk.**

You took your morning pills; that's an accomplishment for sure.

**I certainly did! About that walk.**

It makes me happy when you finish your breakfast. You have eight pounds to gain!

**Maybe it would help if we specified a time for the walk?**

I don't know that you can have a walk just yet.

**I had a feeling you would say that, so I came up with a plan. Here's the plan: drive me to my favorite sniffing spots and let me out of the Raika-Mobile. I'll check on the canine health of the neighborhood, see what Mrs. Mountain Lion has been up to, and then we get back in the Raika-Mobile. Plenty of mental stimulation, and almost no physical exercise. Plus a super comfy mode of travel, since I can rest on the bed. What do you think?**

Hmm. Maybe.

**Maybe?! I cannot live my life with such indecision! And with My Condition, there may not be much life left. Plus, the pills. Remember the pills? A little fresh air will wake my appetite right up! Take me out of the house.**

I'll take you out.

**Perfect.**

Are you going to take your afternoon pills without a fuss?

**Probably not.**

You just said the fresh air would wake up your appetite.

**Sometimes I lie.**

## Mom & Raika

I have wonderful news for you!

**What's that?**

The vet said your bloodwork is absolutely perfect!

**Yeah? Well, I don't know about her.**

You don't like your vet? She's so nice to you!

**She comes in here and puts her hands all over me! Gives me the creeps. Did she say anything else?**

Yes! She's amazed you're fifteen. Says you're very strong and healthy and beautiful for your age, and she feels good about your progress with the new medication. She wants to know your secret.

**She said that? I look amazing and beautiful?**

She did. I think she likes you. She said very few fifteen-year-old dogs are doing as well as you, especially with a heart condition.

**Huh. Amazing and beautiful and very few like me? She's okay, I guess. Did she comment on my butt? I think my butt looks pretty good.**

Maybe not specifically. But she definitely commented on your physical strength and appearance.

**Okay. Good thing she noticed. She's probably a decent vet.**

She also said we're going to make a few medication changes to make you even more comfortable. It's tricky to get it just right.

**Well, I guess that's a good idea, too.**

And she said it's time to go back to your walks. Every day, if we want.

**She said I can go back to my walks? Every day? Did she say how far we could go?**

As far as you and I want to go - no restrictions, besides how you're feeling. She did comment on your weight loss. Basically, I need to offer you three small meals a day, all sorts of nutritious things that you like to eat. You're not taking in enough calories, and we need to do something about that. Maybe with three large snacks, rather than two regular meals per day, we can get a few pounds on you.

**Snacks and unlimited walks? I've always known there was something special about this vet. Can't quite put my finger on it, but she's a good vet. I will admit that after going through a full year of intense dieting only to have to put it back on when I don't actually want to eat makes me feel like I lost an entire year of deliciousness.**

Raika, I apologize for that. The diet was a bit short sighted of me. I really wanted to believe that it mattered. I thought that we would have years and years left if I made sure you got thin again. But all I did was take away one of your greatest pleasures at a time you could have truly appreciated it.

**Well, Mom, on the other hand, look how much better we know each other after all of these fitness walks. You have to admit, we've become pretty amazing friends.**

Yes, Raika, we have become amazing friends indeed. Do you want a snack right now?

**You know, I am feeling a bit hungry. Did the vet say anything about peanut butter pretzels? I think peanut butter pretzels will make a very good third meal.**

Peanut butter pretzels are fine. We'll have that right now before our walk.

**Unlimited walks! What an amazing vet! I do love this vet.**

# Part Three

# Chapter 47:
## Eat the Best Food on the Good Days

### Mom and Raika

You need to stop chasing the cat and the squirrels through the living room window. It's going to kill you. Literally.

**I don't know about that. The vet said just last week that I'm in amazing shape and responding very well to my new medications. Very healthy! Three snacks a day! What an amazing vet!**

I'm serious. You're going to die that way. Drugs help, but they don't make you perfect - just much better. We still need to be careful about sudden exertion. That's where the problem lies, and what still causes your occasional episodes.

**Do you see how the cat takes off when she sees me coming? And the squirrels panic their way right up the trees!**

Raika, what I see is that you can't breathe after you do that and you start falling over. Everyone is trying so hard to get you healthy again, but we need a little cooperation.

**What a great example of perspective. Here I am, focused on the joy of the encounter, and there you are, Negative Nelly, focused on what happens later.**

What happens if I'm not home and you do that? Who's going to help you?

**I can get up, it just takes a while. I'll settle in for a little rest and get up when I'm ready. Plus, it appears that between you, Dad, and the kids, someone is always around to help me out.**

If you pull a muscle, which is really quite likely, I don't know that there's anything we can do for you. You won't be able to get any exercise, and then what would you have left?

**The end started the day I was born - we're just progressing at a more rapid clip now. Anyway, I've been doing this for fifteen years and haven't pulled a muscle yet. I'm not going to change now.**

You stubborn cow.

**I see we have resorted to name calling, widely acknowledged as the lowest form of discussion.**

I'm telling you, Raika. If you keep doing that, it's going to kill you.

**From name calling to threats; might be a tie in the "least likely to influence others" category. I'm disappointed in you. And anyway, you have completely failed to acknowledge the cardiovascular effects of the occasional sprint for exercise.**

Mark my words.

**Can't. I'll be dead.**

You're breaking my heart, Raika. I don't want to fight with you now. I want you to live as long and as healthy as possible. Please... can you try?

**Well, now you're getting to me.**

## Mom & Raika

The vet said we should bring you into the emergency room.

**No.**

I can make you.

**Yes, but can you make me live forever?**

No.

**Then stop with this. Don't let the end of my life be miserable just so you can have a few extra days.**

I can get drugs for your diarrhea over the phone. That means you're going to be up to 14 pills a day.

**That's fine.**

Are you in pain?

**No.**

Do you want to go for a walk?

**Yes.**

Then we will do that instead of going back to the vet. And I'll pick up the drugs. It's not your time yet.

**It's not my time. But I'm sorry I'm making such a mess.**

I don't care about the mess. I care about you being sick.

**I'm okay right now. I'm not in pain, and it's not my time. No matter what happens, I want you to know that I've had an amazing life. Fifteen years of interesting days! I've been all over and done so many things. I've watched you change careers, raise kids, and start a huge business. Now I sleep by your side and go out for exercise when I want to. You've always done what was right for us. Don't stop now.**

A quick trip to the vet could be the solution. They did mention that some of your new medications could cause side effects like diarrhea; they might have more ideas for you.

**The vet cannot cure dying, not even the entire team of specialists. Death is inevitable. You have a responsibility to me. We both know there are no simple answers or the vets would have found them already. Maybe I have one problem that has gotten worse, or maybe I have several**

**problems, but it doesn't matter. I don't want the end of my life to be a slippery slope; first a quick emergency visit where you leave me again, then another round of tests, then just one more procedure, and then the inevitable - death. I want my life to end the same way I have lived it, as happy, engaged, and comfortable as possible. Please don't add just one more thing, and one more thing, and one more thing. I don't want that to be my end.**

I moved up your next routine visit. You can go in sooner. They'll take a look at your heart and lungs and see what else they can do with medication.

**That's fine. But don't leave me there. No more procedures, but more medication is fine. Let's take each day for what it is, and let tomorrow come as it will... Mom? I'm ready for the end when the time comes. You need to be ready, too.**

I'm not ready yet.

**I need you more now, at the end of my life, than I have ever needed you. Please - you have to be ready. You have to get there.**

## Mom & Raika

Well, Raika, look at you, jumping up the steps and being lively.

**I'm feeling good!**

Certainly looks that way. Wonderful to see it! What changed?

**It's a new day.**

I know, but specifically, what changed?

**Getting old and being sick doesn't work that way. You don't just get older and sicker and then fall over dead. You go up and down. You have good days and not so good**

**days. Today is a very fine day, so we should celebrate that rather than trying to figure out what might - or might not - have caused it. You cannot logic your way out of that final hurrah. So out and about we go!**

Don't get me wrong, I could not be happier watching you, but it complicates the process of adjusting to a new normal. Duck and cherries and ice cream for dinner every night is not balanced.

**Are you crazy?! For all we know, that meal last night might have bought me six months!**

Possible, but not likely.

**Well, Mom, here's my point of view: when I'm having good days, let's make them even better. We can do all the fun things, and eat all the tasty foods, so on the days I don't feel so well there's no great loss. I mean, why hold out on the ice cream until I don't feel well enough to enjoy it?**

Nutrition and health?

**One good day and you have completely forgotten about My Condition. It's very serious!**

I'm trying to balance out all the considerations.

**My heart! The pain!**

Are you being serious?

**No. But I need to keep you on your toes.**

That's mean-spirited. Don't do that.

**We're too close to the end for you to lose your sense of humor. You're supposed to say, "You're not dead yet." I say we eat all the best foods on my good days, don't worry about food on the bad days, visit interesting places everyday, smell interesting smells, and see interesting**

**sights.  Plus, don't sweat it too much if the pills don't go down.**

You had me until that last piece.  The pills are going down.

**Eh.  Worth a try.**

You're not dead yet!

**Touché!  So, Mom, being serious for a moment.  Do you really think nutrition matters at this point?**

No, and I won't bring it up again.

Chapter 48:
So Many Pills

## Raika & Mom

**Mom, where are you going?**

For a walk.

**But we just got back from a walk!**

We did. Sadly, my fitness tracker only gave me credit for four minutes of exercise. It says I was standing the rest of the time.

**Piece of junk! I saw your feet moving! They sure don't make things like they used to. You got plenty of exercise.**

Definitely. But I need to go out for a little more.

**If you say so. I recommend that nice trail by the lake. Be home in an hour?**

Dogs aren't allowed there and I was going to bring Brito along.

**Oh. He doesn't need to go. With those short legs of his, he'll end up exhausted. And you're supposed to be getting real exercise! You can leave him here.**

I don't think he would agree with you. He likes going for a walk. I'll leave Lyra here with you for company, and Nick will be doing his homework in the same room as you, so if you need anything, he'll get it for you.

**I still think the walk by the lake would be very nice for you. Really move your feet!**

Brito and I will be home in an hour. Have a nice sleep while we are gone.

**Then will you stay with me for the rest of the day?**

Yes, I'll be home today. Actually, today I have to organize your pills, and it takes a lot of concentration. The new one is twice a day for five days, then down to once a day after that. With food. The little ones go up to three times a day, two each time. No food required for those. These ones here stay the same. And this fat one? You seem to like that one, and I am truly grateful that you eat it on your own, because it is also twice a day. I have to double check the others to make sure I get those right.

**Well, I hope you do get it right. Would be quite a shame if your interpretation of "killing me with kindness" was messing up my medication and taking me out before My Condition got the best of me.**

I'm still struggling with your sense of humor here, but about the pills, I'll get it right. I just need to concentrate.

**Mom, how many pills is this?**

Hmm. Seventeen or eighteen? Something like that.

**That's a lot of pills.**

Raika, after talking to the vet at your last ultrasound appointment, I made some quality of life decisions for you. The good news is that we can probably increase your exercise tolerance and breathing comfort. The bad news is that you'll take more pills and your tummy troubles are likely to continue, plus you'll need another set of tests - but they say I can stay with you the whole time. It was a tradeoff. I hope I did what you would want?

**Yeah, that's good. You don't mean scary or painful tests, right? And yes, going for our walks is more important than tummy troubles. By the way, I do want to mention that the comment you made to the vet about me having a "poodle leg" when they had to shave me - not so funny.**

Well, if they were going to take more blood, I figured you should have matching poodle legs. And you are correct, the tests are not painful. We're done with those painful ones for good.

**Sounds good on the tests. By the way, did you hear what I said when she said the hair would grow back?**

Of course, and I almost mentioned it to the vet. But telling her that you would probably be dead before it grew back seemed awfully morbid. I don't know her very well yet, and maybe she wouldn't understand.

**You could have told her I said it?**

They would have added delusional to the morbid label. I'll pass.

**Do you think I'm her favorite patient yet?**

Probably. I'll have to ask her next time we see her.

**When do I go back?**

In a month. Was it scary?

**No, it was fine. But I'm wondering if maybe we should have some special arrangement.**

Like what?

**Like McDonald's in the waiting room.**

The waiting room would smell like food; they might not appreciate that.

**They won't mind! They know about My Condition. Who denies the last wishes of a dying dog?**

You're not dying.

**Seventeen pills a day, chronic diarrhea, hanging on death's door, and all I want is McDonald's at the vet.**

Okay. McDonald's at the vet.

**You must love me very much.**

Indeed I do, Raika. Indeed I do.

## Raika & Mom

**Brito goes for a hike and I get a bath. Is he dying, too, and no one told me?**

No, he's not dying. And at this exact moment, you're not either. You went for a walk this morning, and you got a bath because you're doing so well that we want you to look your best!

**Does this mean I'm going back to the vet?**

No, you're not going anywhere.

**Exactly. A bath makes no sense if I don't go anywhere.**

Have I ever mentioned you're high maintenance?

**Oh, I'm sorry. I completely forgot that I was supposed to be enthusiastic when I get left behind and the little white dog comes back smelling like the forest.**

You know, I thought of a place I can take you that is forested and shady and not hilly. We can go there tomorrow.

**I'm mollified. A little. So the plan is bacon and eggs for breakfast - good sustenance for a hike - and then a forested, shady, and not-hilly hike?**

Raika, what's up with the bacon and eggs? I never mentioned food at all.

**I know you have it - I saw the groceries on the table! And being as My Condition leaves me at perpetual risk of falling over dead, bacon and eggs seems like a reasonable attempt to head that possibility off at the pass.**

"Bacon and eggs are the perfect food when you have a heart condition!" said no cardiologist ever.

**You're so literal. I am going to ignore the fact that you didn't even ask my cardiologist about food and assume**

**she'd approve. So... bacon and eggs, followed by a forested, shady, not-hilly walk!**

Fine.

**I forgive you for taking out the little white one. But it probably shouldn't happen again.**

Let's focus on your breakfast and walk tomorrow, and worry about the other dogs another day.

**Scrambled.**

What?

**I'd like my eggs scrambled.**

# Part Three

# Chapter 49:
## Night or Day, It's All the Same

## Mom & Raika

Raika, you're going to be the death of us.

**What did I do?!**

Up and down all night!

**I was?  I don't remember that.**

I know, Raika.  You never remember.  I think you made five trips to the backyard to sniff around - but not to pee.

**A sniffing walk at night?  Not a bad idea.  But no, I don't remember.**

So you probably don't remember emptying the garbage in the bathroom?

**Nope.  Don't remember that, either.  That is fun, though. Lots of shredding opportunities in the bathroom trash.**

Huffing at me until I woke up and patted your head?

**Don't remember.  All of this in one night?**

In short, you condensed a full day of activity into six hours... starting at midnight.

**Hmm.  Well, you better get back to work, and I'm going to take a little nap, just in case we're in for another party night.  Amazing how much I'm like the teenagers.**

Amazing.

**Mom, was I worry-old or sick-old or something else?**

This is not the day to ask.  I am simply exhausted, and I'm not sure what to call it.

**How about getting old?**

Indeed.

## Mom & Raika

Raika, you're losing more weight. You need to eat more.

**What you are seeing is weight shift.**

Weight shift?

**Yeah, my weight is shifting down.  Gravity is winning.**

Ah.  I didn't want to say anything about that.

**Well, you don't have to agree with me!  Sometimes a little white lie is the perfect answer.**

I didn't mean gravity is winning - you look fantastic! - you just have a little more definition around your spine and hip bones.  Very athletic.

**It appears the capacity for white lies remains.  I consider that to your favor.**

Regardless, wait till you see what I made you for breakfast.

**Something better than the other dogs are getting?**

Oh, yes!

**What do you have for me?**

A blend of peanut butter, hard-boiled egg, and yogurt!

**That could be tasty.  What flavor is the yogurt?**

I'd have to check.  I think it was plain or maybe honey?

**I'd prefer vanilla, but no worries - just keep it in mind for the future. That still sounds pretty tasty.**

So tasty!

**Wait a second. What's this in the middle?**

That's a flavor capsule.

**I see we're back in the alternate universe. A flavor capsule?**

You haven't even tried it! Plus I froze it to ensure you don't get fish burps.

**A fish-flavored capsule - and you think I'll be pleased. Now I've heard it all.**

If you don't want it, just eat around it.

**It's not that simple! My mouth was all prepped for hard-boiled eggs, peanut butter, and yogurt. Now all I can think about is that fish-flavored capsule in the middle.**

So you're not going to eat it?

**I have an idea. Being as my memory is occasionally a little faulty these days, why don't you scoop out that fish-flavored capsule, put the whole concoction back in the refrigerator for a little while, and try again later? There's a pretty good chance I will forget about it.**

I'll do that!

**Do what?**

What you just said!

**What did I just say?**

We may need to bring the vet out to check on your short-term memory.

I'm joking! See how that works? Go ahead and put my breakfast of hard-boiled eggs, plain or honey yogurt, and peanut butter back in the refrigerator. I'll see it again in thirty minutes.

Chapter 50:
Optimism or Denial

## Raika & Mom

**Hi Mom, whatcha doing?**

Ordering your drugs.

**Don't you think you're getting carried away? That looks like a lifetime supply! Although we may have exceeded that catchy phrase. Get it? Lifetime supply - way past my lifetime!**

It's easier to order large quantities less often - and that's not funny at all.

**Mom, do you know what a progressive disease is?**

You're clarifying my knowledge of the English language now?

**No. Just marveling at the fluid - yet fine - line between optimism, denial, and acceptance.**

My guess is that it's time to adjust your medication again, which is why we're going back to the vet. And since I'm pretty sure she's going to increase your dose, I'm placing the order now. But you're doing well, Raika.

**And that just put you firmly over the line. So here's what I think: the next time we go to the vet, you need to ask her for clarification about the definition of a progressive disease. I don't think you understand my situation very well. You're seeing symptoms because the disease is progressing. That is what happens. I am not normal. Treatment means I am gaining weeks of life so that we can be together longer - but this treatment won't buy me immortality. It won't even buy me years. Sometimes you forget everything you read about my disease when I was**

first diagnosed, so maybe the vet can explain it in a way that you will remember better.

Raika, you go for a two mile walk every day! Dogs on death's door do not go for a two mile walk every day. Everyone says you look amazing. You still move and act like a twelve-year-old dog.

**I have lost 20% of my body weight. I stumble over nothing. And I pass out when I cannot get enough oxygen. What part of that is amazing?**

You're losing weight because you're not eating as much. You need to eat better. And the reason I think the vet will want to increase your medication is to take care of the other symptoms.

**You're not quite grasping what's happening here.**

Raika, right now you're doing fine, or she would've told me that.

**Look at you trying to snatch optimism from the jaws of reality! Regardless, let's go over this once again. I have a progressive disease. That's why my symptoms are coming back. I'd like to think you could see that for yourself, but if you cannot, you need to ask the vet directly so she can explain it to you. Progressive means it is going to get worse. It's time you started paying attention.**

The last time your symptoms got worse, we increased your medication and you were fine again.

**Ask the vet what it means to have a progressive disease. Mom? The average patient lives weeks or maybe months from the point of diagnosis; I've already used up a few months. And Mom, it's been amazing! I'm here with you! Regardless, talking to you is like talking to a brick wall. Promise me you'll ask the vet directly. Ask what is going to happen next. Ask what happens when the drugs don't work anymore, when the dose makes no difference.**

**There will be no miracle here, and we're coming to a time**

**when I am going to need you more than I've ever needed you in my entire life. This is not the time for optimism; I need you to face reality head on.**

I'm not ignoring your symptoms, Raika. We're going to go back to the vet soon. And I'll ask her about your prognosis. I will ask her what is going to happen next.

## Mom & Raika

How you can refuse every bite of food I offer but then scarf down someone's leftover trash is beyond me. You're going to end up with another round of first-class diarrhea.

**My cardiologist said I need probiotics to help with My Condition. Plenty of bacteria in that last load.**

I rather doubt she intended for you to get them that way. The goal is to stop your diarrhea, not to make it worse - and that trash is going to make it a lot worse.

**And there were flavor capsules, as well - perks up my appetite right up!**

What flavor capsules?

**Fillers, salt, preservatives... A treasure trove of possibilities; random reinforcement at its finest!**

How about we buy one of the recommended brands of probiotics instead?

**You know, my cardiologist said I need to stop losing weight. In my opinion, discouraging my lucky finds and budget probiotics is shortsighted. Look at me consuming additional calories! First, I check all the regular places, but every once in a while I get lucky. I catch a scent on the air, wait till you're not looking, and lickety-split! I head in that direction and recover some fantastic morsel, only a few days old, just waiting for me to find it and eat it**

**up!**

When I have to bathe your butt, you may have a different opinion.

**My cardiologist mentioned keeping me happy. Scavenging keeps me happy. Washing my butt does not keep me happy.**

Your cardiologist never said a word about keeping you happy.

**Yes, she did. When you went out of the room.**

I never went out of the room.

**Not even a quick bathroom trip?**

Raika.

**Worth a try.**

## Chapter 51:
### New Vet for an Old Dog

## Raika & Mom

**A bath at my age is wholly inappropriate.**

No, it's not.

**How can you say that? What if I had died right there in the tub? You would've felt terrible. Which you should.**

I waited until it was one of your good days to give you a bath.

**I only have so many good days left, and you used one up on a bath!**

Followed by a walk!

**You skipped right over the brushing. The bath was followed by brushing, and you know brushing bothers my skin.**

And all of that was followed by a slow, meandering walk. So not so bad?

**Look at you being the eternal optimist. By my count, two things were miserable, and only the walk was good.**

Well, you look lovely.

**I can't take that with me.**

I gave you duck for dinner!

**True. That was tasty.**

And did I mention that your new vet is coming to meet you tomorrow? I thought you should look nice for her.

**Ah, now we get to the heart of the matter. The bath was to**

**impress the vet.**

Well, that's at least partially true. We want her to know that you are well-cared for, and that's how humans show they care! Through things like baths and keeping your nails trimmed.

**She's probably going to want to touch me. Why does she have to do that, anyway?**

I don't think she can do much of an exam from across the room.

**I feel fine.**

I know you do. That's why she's coming now - to get to know you. And to make sure you keep on feeling fine. She specializes in old dogs, so she knows all about dogs like you.

**Old dogs? I'm reasonably resigned to this.**

Well, not just old dogs. She's a vet who specializes in end-of-life care: a hospice vet. She's going to help make sure that all of your days are as good as possible now. And I really need the help, Raika. I'm afraid I'm not able to do it on my own anymore. You're maxed out on all your medications. I need more help to keep you comfortable.

**Methinks you asked the cardiologist how much longer I might be here. That's good, Mom. I hope you know I'm not afraid, but I am terribly sad that I am going to leave you soon. I love you very much.**

# Chapter 52:
## The Bucket List

## Mom & Raika

What did you think of your new vet?

> **She's a good one. She didn't even try to touch me until it was almost time to leave. Plus, she supported peanut butter pretzels as a suitable bedtime snack. I would like to point out that she did require additional snacks as frequently as possible throughout the day.**

I don't think she required it, but she did suggest giving you any snacks that you'll eat to help with your acid tummy.

> **I would call that a requirement. When the vet suggests something, it's a requirement.**

I'm glad you feel that way, because she also suggested bloodwork to check a few things.

> **Sometimes I should just keep my mouth shut. I wonder if I still have time to learn that?**

Doubtful. On another note, I want to bring up something else she mentioned. She suggested we talk about a bucket list.

> **A bucket list? Does this mean I'm on death's door?**

No, it means there are things we might want to do before you are on death's door - while you can still do them and enjoy yourself.

> **Can I go back to the park and play fetch?**

As much as I would like to take you, I think that would effectively be pushing you through the aforementioned doorway. I'm sorry I didn't think of a bucket list earlier, but it's too late for fetch now.

> **It's okay, Mom. I've played in many parks; I can visualize**

**what it was like and be good with it.**

Thank you, Raika.

**I've thought of my first bucket list activity.**

What's that?

**I want to go for a walk on the sand trail.**

The sand trail?

**Yes, the second half of our old walk. I haven't been there in more than a year, not since they quit allowing dogs. I don't know what it looks like anymore! That's a long time not to smell all of the important spots. I would like to go for a walk on the sand trail.**

We could do that. Drive there and start our walk from the beginning of the trail and have Dad pick us up on the other end. It might be a little hard, but it's possible.

**Any thoughts about the ranger? Not allowing dogs on that trail anymore?**

If we get a ticket, I'll pay it.

**Tomorrow?**

Tomorrow. Tomorrow, we'll take a walk on the sand trail.

**I'm looking forward to it.**

Excellent.

**How many things can I have on my bucket list?**

As many as you can think up.

**I'm going to start thinking about it. I'll let you know for sure.**

Do that, Raika. And we'll work our way through that list.

## Mom & Raika

Raika, last night was like living with the worst dog on the planet.

**Say it isn't so!**

Wandering around the house like a ghost and stumbling into walls. No one got any sleep.

**I don't remember that.**

You didn't go to sleep until after four! Walking up to people, breathing in their faces, tapping on them with your foot. Totally not fun, Raika.

**That's really quite hard to imagine. Especially since I have such a comfy dog bed right there!**

You certainly weren't using it.

**I just can't imagine what happened. Did you feed me something different? Forget to pat me and wish me a good sleep before I went to bed? I do like my routines, you know.**

Nope. It was all the same.

**Regardless, I don't quite understand the problem. It's not like I was asking you to explore the house with me.**

With all that thumping and bumping and getting stuck, we have to stay awake to help get you out of your various predicaments. Plus, we worry about you; you're obviously distressed.

**Totally mystifying!**

And you picked a heckuva night for it. I wasn't feeling well last night; I couldn't even manage our walk yesterday.

**What do you mean, you couldn't manage our walk? Did I not get my walk?**

No, I was sick, so we stayed home.

**Well, I certainly don't mean to shame you - though I kind of do - but how can you expect me to sleep at night if I don't get my walk during the day? How many steps did I miss out on? Four thousand or so? I had to spend the first seven hours of the night making them up!**

Every time I tried to go to sleep, I started feeling sick again. And then I'd wake up because of you.

**In addition to missing out on four thousand steps of walking, I didn't get to sniff stuff. And we know how soothing that is to the brain, and how it aids with relaxation.**

Plus I was sweating! First hot, then cold. Just miserable.

**A good dose of exercise, some mental stimulation, and an opportunity to make sure all is well in the world. Walks are really not optional.**

So there I am, lying on my bed, sweating and dizzy - did I tell you I was dizzy? - getting up every few minutes to fix your latest problem. And that went on until four! In the morning!

**And then the floods and locusts came?**

What?

**Nevermind. Anyway, make sure I get my walk every day; I need plenty of mental and physical exercise! Then I think we'll be fine.**

I'll definitely make sure you get your walk today. I'd prefer not to see an encore performance.

**Well, not now. I'm exhausted. I got practically no sleep last night.**

## Mom & Raika

Look at you, all awake and cheerful after your four hour nap and new walking adventure.

**That was certainly a fine walk - so many new smells! How fast did we go?**

Looks like we did forty-eight minute miles and covered a total of 1.3 miles.

**Is that fast?**

Adjusted for your age group, it's very fast indeed! Although realistically, there aren't too many in your age group. Do you remember the old lab we saw? I didn't ask how old he was, but I thought you were faster than him.

**Yeah, I did pretty well. I feel good! Plus, I thought of another bucket list activity.**

What's that?

**Frozen yogurt, family style**

You've never joined the family for frozen yogurt.

**I know! All these years, watching the family go out after dinner for frozen yogurt. I want to come along.**

That's more of a summer activity, so we better do it soon before it gets cold.

**No time like the present.**

All right, tonight we'll do a family trip for frozen yogurt. And after that, you will sleep! Wait till you see your sleeping area. You have a cute little turtle nightlight, a pillow, and your own fan. Plus one extra pill and a little snack. So, sleepy thoughts, okay?

**Okay. Sleepy thoughts. Head on pillow... eyes closed...**

**pat, pat, pat... and off I go to sleep!**

Exactly. Head on pillow... eyes closed... pat, pat, pat... and off you go!

# Chapter 53:
## The End of Conversation

## Mom & Raika

We need a new plan.

**Mmm?**

If we don't all get some sleep tonight, we're going to start to hallucinate.

**Mmm.**

I'm glad you're sleeping now. It was terrible watching you, Raika. You're so tired. So get lots of sleep now, and then we'll go for a walk. Then one more walk before you go to bed, just a short one, and the vet has prescribed medication for you. We need to solve this or you're going to start coming unraveled. You cannot go without sleep. Raika, are you listening?

**Mmm-hmm.**

If the medication doesn't work, we'll create a soft area for you so you can't get hurt. Maybe a pen around your bed with lots of pillows, or you can go in a big crate where you'll be safe. And a fan, too - that might help. Okay? It's okay if you don't want to talk now. Get some sleep. We'll take a walk in a few hours. Sleep will make you feel better. And then a little exercise. Now that I think about it, we can do one of the bucket list walks that you requested; we'll go to Mrs. Mountain Lion's rock. Then dinner. Then rest, a little medication, and then we sleep for the night.

## Mom

Good morning, Raika. I thought last night went a little bit better? There's room for improvement, but this is a process of trial and error.

I'm glad we went out for yogurt, even if you didn't eat yours. I saw you looking around with your ears up. So now you know what the family does when we go out at night; we eat yogurt, and watch the people, and talk about whatever comes up.

We talked about you. How important you have been in my life. First, you taught me about dog training, and then you taught me about looking at life through the eyes of a dog. Next, you taught me about companionship and simply being with another being that shares a common history. Finally, you will teach me about going on - preparing meals for the other dogs, even when your bowl is not there.

After I let you out this morning, I checked from the kitchen window to see what you were doing. You were staring into the distance, oblivious to Lyra impatiently running in circles for her breakfast. When I opened the door to let you in, you just stood there looking through the glass. You could've come in the house if you had walked to the other side of the door. As I considered it, I realized that this has been going on for a while; your nighttime confusion is starting to bleed into your days, as well.

I thought about what it means to have quality of life; is it more than the absence of pain? More than simply existing?

And then you went to the trash and started pulling paper out of the wastebasket, picking and choosing the best pieces before returning with them to your bed. Raika, I knew that was it right there. Quality of life is caring which piece of paper you shred next. Staying awake to watch the people walk by while everyone else eats yogurt. Forty-eight minute miles when we go to a new place because you want to sniff all the smells and know who's been there before you showed up, because you still care to know.

It's not your time yet, Raika. But it's coming. Each day I will ask myself if you still care which paper you should shred next. I will watch you watch the world when we go to a new place, and I will ask myself, do you still care about being here?

And when you no longer care - when you stare off into the distance and you don't care to see what is in front of you, or to smell where the other dogs have been? - that's when I'll know we're at the end, that life has no more quality for you.

I hope you get some good sleep today. Next on your bucket list is the beach. I know of one that has sand close to the car. We will go there today.

## Raika

**Good morning, Mom. I tried to thank you for my beach day yesterday, but I don't think you heard me. I don't even know if you can hear me now. I wanted to tell you that I loved every minute of it! I loved looking out the window of the Raika-Mobile, walking on the beach with you and Dad, eating my chalupa, and then sleeping all the way home.**

**I think maybe it made me so tired that I'm not able to talk to you right now. I want you to know that I'm trying to say thank you, and that I love you, but I'm really very tired. So today I will sleep. I might even sleep through our regular walk time, but don't wake me up. Just let me sleep.**

**If you want, you can go for a walk. It's important that you get your exercise, too. And it would be okay if you took one of the other dogs along for company.**

## Mom

Hello, Raika. Are you listening to me? Raika, I want to tell you that I talk to the vet every day - sometimes several times a day. We've maxed out all your medications. We've tried to keep you comfortable at night, but you continue to panic and struggle. Nothing is helping.

Raika, this vet might specialize in hospice, but she won't tell me when it's time. That's not her job. That means I need to be the one to make that decision; I have to decide what is the right thing for you, and when that needs to happen. I see you sleeping peacefully here on your bed, but you don't talk to me anymore. I had counted on the fact that you were going to tell me, that you would say, "It's time." But you've stopped talking. Is this what you meant when you said I would have to be strong enough to make a decision? Did you know you would no longer be able to speak for yourself?

You don't want to walk, even if I carry you down the driveway. And when I give you a full wastepaper basket full of your favorite shredding paper, you simply watch as Lyra comes and takes it away, one piece at a time, until the basket is empty again.

Raika, do you remember our conversation when I said that I hoped you would just fall asleep and not wake up when it was your time? I've been thinking about that this past week. I was hoping that one day I would come to your side, and rather than finding you asleep, I would find you had left - in peace, and on your own. But that's not going to happen, is it? You can carry on without enough oxygen to walk, and without enough will to move. So much of your body and mind have left, but your soul refuses to follow.

# Chapter 54:
## Goodbye, Raika

### Mom

Raika, you were special the day you were born. Always there. Always willing. Always giving more than I ever expected or hoped for. Always by my side, watching me. Waiting. For so many years, I loved you for all that you gave me.

Then it was time for you to retire, and we were stuck, not sure how to spend our time together without a goal to reach, or a competition to focus on. I fed you too much and played too little, ignoring the fact that what you really wanted was my attention.

So we started walking, and that's when I began to truly appreciate you for who you are, rather than for what you could do. I watched you being a dog, and I marveled at what that was, to be a dog. I began to share you with the world so others could marvel along with me. And I loved you a little more than before.

Then age and illness slowed you down, and our lives took yet another turn. Our walks became less about exploring the world and more about being together. Quiet daily rituals that wound around our days. And still, my heart found even more love.

This past week, for the first time since you were born, there was nothing more. You have nothing to show me. Nothing to take. Nothing to share. You've given me everything you have to give, and taken all that you can hold.

You're so tired. Raika, I can see that you're so tired. And because I love you as much as you have loved me, I am ready.

Remember those molecules you promised me? The ones we talked about a year ago? Don't forget, because I will need them more than you could possibly imagine.

I am not going to think about tomorrow, but today, because I love you the most that I have ever loved you, I'm letting you go.

Raika 05/24/04 - 10/15/19

## Chapter 55:
### And Now We Walk Alone

### Mom

Good morning, Raika.

Today is cold and the dark of winter is coming. I know you loved the cold, but I'm glad you left when it was still warm. I wish the warm weather would last just a little longer so I can stay out of the house. I don't want to be in the house without you under my desk where I could keep an eye on you. Or maybe you were keeping an eye on me. Both, probably.

So I will go for a walk. Should I bring a dog? No, I don't want to be with a dog. Maybe I will walk in a place that doesn't allow dogs. Maybe you will be there with me, and I just won't see you. That's what I'll do - go alone and maybe you will be there.

I took your pills off the counter. It made me dizzy and nauseous. I'll wait a little longer to wash your dog beds.

I don't know if I mentioned it to you, but I started a to-do list recently. I'm thinking it's a good thing, because I can't structure myself very well right now. I looked at the list; you're on it several times. Walk Raika. Clean Raika. Organize Raika's pills. I took all of those things off. I don't want to see them.

Last night I kept looking over the edge of the bed where you slept. I've been doing that for so long that it's a part of me. I always liked to see you sleeping quietly, breathing easily. It made me feel like things were okay in the world. Last night I couldn't stop myself from looking, even though I knew you would not be there. I looked anyway. And you were not there. I knew that.

Soon I'll have Dad take your dog bed away from my side of the bed. I'm afraid Lyra will sleep on it, and I don't want to see her there. So if you are watching and you see that it is gone, I want you to know why.

I don't know where you are now, Raika. Somewhere on your new journey, I guess. I know in my heart that you're comfortable. I may not know where you are, but I know that you're comfortable. Breathing easily. Moving freely. Sleeping quietly.

I know I didn't let you suffer, Raika, but now I find myself second guessing myself. Did I do the right thing at the right time? I wonder if I should have held on for a few more days - not that it would have changed anything. I try to remind myself that your life ended the way I had hoped it would: full with life each day, planning for the future, and then such a fast decline that there was no time left at all. Even so, I find myself wondering if I could have had a few more days.

I can't believe how quiet the house is. I don't understand that; you never made any noise, but the change is palpable anyway. The other dogs know you're gone. I don't know if they miss you, but they know you're not here, and somehow, knowing you're not here is making them quiet. Are you giving your molecules away already? Did you give Brito some quietness?

Today it's hard for me to breathe. I know that tomorrow will be better. And I know that the day after that will be better still. But today it's hard to breathe.

If you can hear me, know that I am thinking about you constantly, and that I hope that your journey is going well.

Love, Mom

## Mom

Good morning, Raika.

Lyra looked for you today. She checked each dog bed, the pantry where you sometimes ate your snacks, and under my desk. I don't know how she felt when she didn't find you.

Brito seems to be dribbling pee in his sleep. I'll get him to the vet to see what's happening there, but I'll admit that my first thought was that I hoped you hadn't given him molecules for incontinence. And then I thought about what you would've said to me; you would've scolded me for being so blatantly disrespectful of your declining body. "What a thing to say! It's like you were raised in a barn!"

But you're not here, so I'll just apologize now. It's not polite to make fun of you. It wasn't polite before you left, and apparently I'm not much better now.

On my walk yesterday, I listened to music, mostly old 70s songs. Do you remember the song "Tie A Yellow Ribbon Round the Old Oak Tree"? The gist of it is that this guy got out of jail and he didn't know if his partner would want him back, so she was supposed to tie a yellow ribbon around the oak tree in the front of the house if he could return. As the song ends, he's on the bus and he asks the bus driver to look and see if it's there because he can't look for himself. And it is - hundreds of them! And the whole bus is cheering for him, happy that he is going to be okay.

As I listened to that song, I thought about what it means when a community supports another who is afraid, distressed, or just plain hurting. In my mind, I'm on a boat, alone in one of the rooms. There's a huge leak in the floor. I could drown in that room, but I won't because there is a gap under the door where the water goes out and fills the rest of the boat. On the other side of the door, there is an endless supply of people furiously removing the water as fast as it comes in so that I won't drown. I cannot see them, and I am not ready to speak to them, but I need them. I am grateful for their help. I know they will keep me afloat until I'm ready to open the door, walk out, and take care of myself.

I could do that - stand up and walk out. But I'm too tired to do that right now. Soon I will, but not today. So if you're watching and worrying about me, remember that I have a community around me that is supporting me as best they can. Dad and Nick and Chris all love me and are taking good care of me. My friends are watching and taking care of me, too. I am not alone. But you're not here.

I hope your journey is going well. We never talked about this part - the steps of leaving. Maybe you knew the answers and I forgot to ask. Maybe not. And now you can well and truly say to me, "You have no idea what you're talking about."

That's worth something, I bet.

Love, Mom

## Raika

Mom! Mom? Can you hear me? Mom, there are many things I'd like to tell you, but I don't have much time, so I'll get to the important part right away.

I was wrong about molecular distribution. I was right about how it works, but I was wrong about being able to say where the molecules should go. The fact is, the decision is made by committee, and not by me. By committee! We all know how things can go wrong when a committee gets involved - too many cooks in the kitchen! So of course I put in my appeal right away.

Today my appeal was heard. The judge was not on my side. He started out a very grumpy guy, a total rule follower! But I was not about to give up, so I told him all about our situation. I explained how I had promised that most of my molecules should go directly to you, because I was sure you were going to need them. I told him that you were counting on me. Well, you know me, I can be absolutely charming when I need to - and I was! It took a bit of doing, but I wore him down. Soon he was throwing my ball and sharing his sandwich, and then we got down to business.

Mom, after haggling back and forth and making my case, we made arrangements. We went through all of the molecules one at a time. There were paper shredding molecules, determined molecules, optimistic molecules, cheerful molecules, joyous molecules, kind molecules, relaxing molecules, and working molecules. There were molecules for energy! Molecules for health, and strength, and beauty! We assigned them all. We gave them away like candy all over the world to dogs and people who might need them, and who were trying to do better - ready to see the world with fresh eyes and an open heart.

And while we were rolling along and the judge was smiling and cooperating, I asked that we hold back a sizable chunk of molecules, evenly balanced between my best and worst traits, for whatever puppy might show up for you to love next. Those molecules will remain here, ready and waiting, until your next puppy goes through molecular acquisition day.

Unfortunately, there was a bit of a problem when I brought up the quiet molecules for Brito. In short, no one thinks there's a snowball's chance in hell that I can give him enough to make a difference, so there's your heads up. Sorry, but I did try.

Even after giving so many away, it was obvious that there would be plenty of molecules left over for you. They will be lodged directly in your heart, with just a small hole remaining to let the grief flow out. That's important because we don't want it bottled up inside.

Mom? Know that I love you so much! And you're going to be okay! You're going to have lots of molecules, and they even agreed to rush delivery, so I'd expect them to start arriving in a day or two. Just remember that all of our conversations and walks, every minute we spent together - that's who we are. We are Team Raika! We will always be a team, but now it will be in your heart and your memories, and that will be forever.

So, here's the part I dread telling you. There was a cost. In exchange for having a say about where my molecules would go, I had to agree to give up talking to you forever. I offered up everything else I could think of; take away my duck and cherry treats, my swimming pool, my wastepaper basket for shredding. Take away my walks, and my games of fetch and tug. Take it all! But they held firm. Stop talking or no deal.

Mom, this is the most painful thing I have ever had to do. But because I have loved you as much as you have loved me, I have listened.

I remembered those molecules I promised you. The ones we talked about a few years ago. I did not forget, because I knew you would need them more than I could possibly imagine.

I cannot think about tomorrow, but today, because I love you the most that I have ever loved you, now I let you go.

# Epilogue

## Mom

As with all things that I took from Raika, my ability to connect with the vastness of the world, and all that it has to offer, ebbs and flows - presumably as a function of my own self attempting to both incorporate her wisdom, while simultaneously pushing back into a more familiar space. Some days I remain too focused on work, whereas other days I find myself slowing down and appreciating the complexity of the larger world around me. I suppose I received molecules for seeking out adventure and slowing down to take in what is around me - in uneven doses, and often in conflict.

Regardless, most days I walk. I may walk with another dog, a family member, or on rare occasions, I may walk alone. I may hold the cell phone and work, but just as often I leave it undisturbed in my pocket.

Last week I stepped over a dead tree, one that had fallen in a recent storm and exposed the rotten roots underneath. I wasn't surprised to see that tree lying across the path; Raika had told me it would fall, that the beetles had worked their way under the bark, that its time was near and that the tree was dying.

Raika could not give me the molecules that would have allowed me to smell what she could smell, though no doubt she tried. I cannot smell the beetles or the family of mice that moved in at an opportune time, but I can recognize the cycle taking place within and around all of us. I know that one piece of life dies so that another can live.

Instead, Raika gave me the gift of appreciation, to know just how much I had missed. To know that there is knowledge that I will never have access to, and that that knowledge that is hidden from me may be absolutely obvious to a dog, a mouse, or a beetle. I'm okay with that. I can choose to pay attention and know a little bit more than I would have known otherwise, and that is enough.

On days when I become wrapped up in the fast pace of life, with

deadlines to meet and tasks that need to be done, I feel that I
have moved on and I forget Raika for a time. And yet, another
day follows, and as I watch a dog engrossed in sniffing a rock,
I remember Raika in vivid detail. I remember her soft fur, her
watchful eyes, and her quiet awareness of all that happened around
her. I remember walking in the rain, wondering what possessed us to
head out, and coming back thoroughly drenched yet content that we
made that choice. On those days, I miss my dog as if the loss were
only yesterday, and I wonder if I will ever truly leave her behind.

When I walk, I feel the connection to others and to the world as a
whole as it shifts around me - and that is when I remember to be
grateful to a much-loved dog who changed the course of my life.

# Author's Note

While this story is a work of fiction, Raika was a real dog with a real personality: opinionated, aware, and exceptionally devoted to me. The weight loss, regular exercise, irregular eating patterns, vacillating health, and the nighttime issues - they were real, as well.

As I wrote her stories, I published them on Facebook. As a result, Raika came to the end of her life with thousands of fans rooting for her - and for me. We cried together when the inevitable end of her life took away one of the best friends I ever had.

In the process of sharing her, I opened up my heart to the world, giving voice to our private struggles in a public forum. This led me to understand the truly universal reality of living with - and loving - an old dog. Mental confusion, struggles with food, and endless trips to the vet are par for the course, as is the tortuously difficult decision making that takes place when you love too much to let go, even when the suffering you see in front of you is too real to ignore.

Canine Cognitive Dysfunction (CCD) is a common yet relatively unknown medical condition that affects many pets. If you're living with an older dog who is struggling to sleep at night, getting confused within their own home, reverting to puppy-like house training issues, and barking at everything and nothing, there's a good chance you're struggling with CCD. In addition to bringing up your concerns with your veterinarian, one resource which you might find helpful is the book "Remember Me? Loving and Caring for a Dog with Canine Cognitive Dysfunction" by Eileen Anderson. There are also active social media groups that provide support for people living with dogs struggling with this disorder. Sometimes, recognizing that you are not alone can make all the difference when you're trying to incorporate rational decision making at a time when your heart is feeling anything but logical.

After engaging a hospice veterinarian for Raika's final weeks, I truly cannot imagine struggling through the end of a dog's life without this support. These veterinarians specialize in end-of-life care and work in conjunction with your regular veterinarian to provide maximum comfort and support while focusing on both quantity and quality of life. To find a hospice veterinarian near you, reach out to The International Association for Animal Hospice and Palliative Care.

Dogs, much like people, do not simply get older and sicker and then pass away. They have good days, great days, and terrible days. We can make choices at the end of their lives to allow them to leave this earth with as much dignity, and as little suffering, as possible, but it's hard to do - one of the hardest things you will ever do. I know. I tried to do that for Raika.

If you have lost a beloved pet recently, or if you know that the time may be near, I hope that by sharing her with you, I have helped you as well. I wish you only the best on your unique journey. May the knowledge of those molecules that you will soon receive, lodged directly in your heart, provide you with a source of comfort.

## About the Author

Denise Fenzi is a professional dog trainer who specializes in building cooperation, joy, and extreme precision in competition dog sports teams. In addition to traveling worldwide to teach dog training conferences and seminars, Denise writes non-fiction prolifically for the dog sports audience, and more recently, fiction for all audiences who share her love for dogs. In addition, Denise runs a very successful online school for both competition and pet dogs, the Fenzi Dog Sports Academy.

Denise currently lives with her husband, Millo, and two teenaged sons, Chris and Nick. Her canine companions include Lyra, Brito, and most recently, Dice.

You can find all of her books at www.thedogathlete.com, her school at www.fenzidogsportsacademy.com and her blog at www.denisefenzi.com. Denise also participates avidly on Facebook, both on her personal wall, Denise Fenzi, and on Raika's book page, Conversations with Raika. Feel free to meet her there and introduce yourself!